Contents

How to use this book   V
Finding the information you need   V

Introduction
What is GNVQ?   VI
What is Foundation GNVQ Health and Social Care? VI
How do you learn on your GNVQ?   VI
How is your GNVQ assessed?   VI

Toolkit

General information
Study skills   2
Solving problems   2
Carrying out research   3
Writing questionnaires   4
Health and safety   5

Communication
Listening skills   6
Talking skills   7
Talking on the telephone   7
Making presentations   7
Body language   9
Writing skills   10
Memoranda (memos)   11
Using images   12
Simple reports   12

Application of Number and Information Technology
Percentages   13
VAT   13
Discounts   14
Pictorial presentation   16
Bar charts   16
Pictograms   18
Measure   19
Systems of measurement   19
Metric and Imperial   20
Paper   20
Conversion   22
Conversion factors   22
Conversion tables   22
Conversion graphs   23
Using information technology   24
Using a spreadsheet   24
Producing graphs   24
Safety first   26
The mean, the mode and the range
The mean   27
The mode   27
The range   28
Answers   29

Form for you to fill in
Application form   30

Unit 1: Understanding health and well-being
Plan how to improve health and well-being 31
Why do we need to improve health and well-being? 32
What makes us healthy?   32
Diet   32
A balanced diet   34
Exercise   36
Recreational activities   39
Assignment: Planning to improve health and well-being 41
Case study: Jason   41
Case study: Ellen   41
Quiz: How much do you know about planning to improve health and well-being? 43

Investigate risks to health   44
Basic health needs   44
Client groups   46
Basic health needs   46
Infants   46
Main risks to health   47
Alcohol misuse   47
Smoking   48
Drug misuse   49
Drug abuse   49
Effects of a poor diet   50
Effects of too much fat, sugar and salt   50
Effects of too little fibre, vitamins and minerals 51
Poor personal hygiene   51
Unsafe sexual behaviour   54
Lack of exercise   55
The risks in public and private settings 56
Major life changes   57
The effects of changes   57
Case study: Rabena   58
Coping with change   59
Finding time to relax   60
Support from others   60
Personal care   60
Assignment: The Park View Centre   61
Quiz: How much do you know about investigating risks to health? 62
Answers   63

Unit 2: Understanding personal development and relationships
Investigate personal development   64
How do people develop?   65
Life stages   66
Main life stages   66
Infancy   66
Childhood   69
2 ½ to 5 year olds   70

5 to 10 year olds 72
Adolescence 74
Adulthood 76
Old age 78
Social and economic factors affecting personal development 80
Social factors 80
Case study: Jamal 82
Economic factors 83
Case study: Melanie 83
Case study: Jennie and Paul 85
Assignment: Life span chart 86
Quiz: How much do you know about personal development? 88

Explore relationships at different life stages 89
Relationships 89
What different relationships are there? 90
Friendships 91
Working relationships 93
Sexual relationships 94
Parent-child relationships 94
Relationships at different life stages 96
What's so good about relationships? 96
Why do relationships go wrong? 97
Case study: Chloe 98
Assignment: Relationships chart 100
Quiz: How much do you know about exploring relationships? 102

Explore relationships between clients and carers 103
Making effective relationships 103
What makes an effective relationship? 103
Respect 104
Recognition of individual identity 104
Client choice 105
Confidentiality 106
Practical ways of setting up and keeping an effective relationship 106
Barriers to effective relationships 108
Ways of breaking down barriers 108
Carers 109
The needs of clients 109
Meeting needs 109
In what ways can carers help meet client's needs? 109
Case studies 113
Assignment: Clients and carers 114
Case study: Joanna 114
Case study: Sadik 114
Quiz: How much do you know about exploring relationships between client and carer? 115

Unit 3: Investigate working in health and social care

Investigate working in health and social care services in the UK 116
Who provides health care? 117
National Health Service and Social Services 117
Social services care 118
Private care 119
Community services 120

Case study: Jenny's accident 121
Job roles in health and social care 122
What are the main purposes of job roles in health and medical care? 124
Job roles in community care and support 126
Job roles in indirect care 128
Assignment: Mr and Mrs Underwood 130
Case study: Mr and Mrs Underwood 130
Quiz: How much do you know about working in health and social care? 132

Investigate jobs in health and social care 132
What shall I do when I leave school or college? 132
Suitable jobs for suitable people 133
Suiting you 134
Understanding yourself 134
Developing your self-awareness 136
Qualities needed in a caring job 137
Suitable jobs 137
Where to get help, advice and information 137
Training for care work 138
Ways to gain qualifications 138
Assignment: Which job first? 141
Quiz: How much do you know about investigating jobs? 142

Plan for employment in health and social care 143
Where do I get advice and information? 144
The main stages in job recruitment 145
Five point plan of recruitment 145
Ways of presenting personal information 146
Your CV 147
National record of achievement 148
How do I fill in application forms? 150
How do I find out what to do at the interview? 151
Assignment: The careers exhibition 152
Quiz: Check your knowledge of planning for employment 153

Useful addresses 154

Quiz answers 155

Core skills coverage grid 156

Index 157

Acknowledgements 161

How to use this book

This book contains information, ideas and activities for Foundation GNVQ Health and Social Care students. It covers:

- the three mandatory units (Units 1, 2 and 3)
- the level 1 core skills in Application of Number, Communication and Information Technology
- vocabulary and skills you will find useful throughout your GNVQ, and when you start work or go on to take another course.

Finding the information you need

You will see that this book is divided into four main sections:

- the Toolkit. This contains general information on how to approach GNVQ assignments and activities; advice to help you achieve the core skills units in Application of Number, Communication and Information Technology; photocopy sheets to help you with activities.
- Unit 1: Understanding health and well-being
- Unit 2: Understanding personal development and relationships
- Unit 3: Investigate working in health and social care

Each of the Unit sections covers all the elements, performance criteria and range statements you need to understand for your GNVQ.

Recognising symbols

This book uses symbols to help you find different types of information and activities. Look out for the following:

What to look for:	What it means
	Activity. There is an activity on most pages to help you practise skills and find out more information.
	Case study. Some sections include case studies to help you understand how things work in the real world of health and social care.
	Assignment. At the end of every element there is an assignment. If you complete this assignment, you will produce some useful evidence for your portfolio.
	Quiz. Quizzes are included for fun, but they are a useful way to show how well you have understood the information in the mandatory units.

What to look for:	What it means
	Question. Something for you to think about, or a question for you to answer.
	What does it mean? An explanation of words used in health and social care which might be new to you.
	More information. Often, topics are covered in more than one place in this book. Where it would be useful for you to look at another page for more information, you will see this symbol.

Introduction

What is GNVQ?

GNVQ stands for General National Vocational Qualification. All GNVQ qualifications cover a broad area of the world of work, such as 'health and social care', 'manufacturing' or 'leisure and tourism'. Each year, tens of thousands of students take GNVQ courses.

You can take GNVQs at three levels:

- Foundation
- Intermediate
- Advanced

You are studying for a **Foundation GNVQ**. This can:

- help you decide which career to follow
- prepare you for your chosen career
- give you a nationally recognised qualification
- put you on the ladder to further qualifications.

When you have completed your Foundation GNVQ in Health and Social Care, you will probably either find employment or go on to an Intermediate GNVQ (this could be in Health and Social Care or another GNVQ area).

What is Foundation GNVQ in Health and Social Care?

Foundation GNVQ in Health and Social Care is about what people in the Caring Services do and the skills they need.

These skills include:

- knowing about the area of Health and Social Care and the work it includes
- learning about the client groups and what affects their health and well-being
- understanding how personal development and relationships can affect clients
- communicating well, working with numbers, and working with information technology.

Your GNVQ – and this book – will introduce you to all of these skills, and will put you on the road to developing them for yourself.

How do you learn on your GNVQ?

You will already have realised that studying for a GNVQ is different to studying for a GCSE. This is partly because it is about work outside school or college, but it is also because the course is written in terms of performance criteria, range statements and evidence indicators.

Your teacher will have a full copy of what you need to achieve for your GNVQ, and during the course you will probably be given a copy as well. You will need this so you can plan how to show you have gained the skills, knowledge and understanding described in the evidence indicators.

You already know that you need to be organised in order to collect and store the evidence of your achievements in a portfolio. You also need to organise your own learning through 'action planning'. This does not mean your teacher is out of a job; but it does mean that you will have more say than ever before in how you learn.

Action planning takes place every time you tackle a new topic. Your teacher will suggest assignments to you that are related to the evidence indicators, and you will be asked to plan an assignment – either on your own, or as part of a group. You need to make sure that your work covers the evidence indicator.

How is your GNVQ assessed?

Your GNVQ is assessed in two ways.

- You collect your coursework in a portfolio of evidence, which you have to organise carefully so it meets the evidence indicators. Your teacher will help you do this, but you are responsible for the portfolio so you must be well organised. This portfolio is then assessed to make sure that you have covered all the performance criteria and range statements for each unit, and that you have met the evidence indicators.
- You take three one-hour short answer tests covering the three mandatory units. If you don't pass these first time you can take them again, but you must pass them in order to achieve your GNVQ.

Toolkit

Introduction

This Toolkit contains information to help you work towards your Foundation Health and Social Care GNVQ. As you read this book, you will probably find it useful to look back to this section for ideas, advice and information.

The Toolkit includes:

- general information on how to approach GNVQ assignments and activities
- advice and information to help you achieve the core skills units in Communication, Application of Number and Information Technology

General information

This section looks at some of the skills and knowledge you will need for your GNVQ. It includes information on:

- study skills – how to approach your GNVQ course
- carrying out research – how to find the information you need for assignments and activities
- health and safety – how you are protected in your place of work by the Health and Safety at Work Act.

It also includes a section on health and safety, which plays a vital part in caring for people in any setting.

Study skills

As soon as you start your Foundation GNVQ, you will probably find that you need to study in new ways. You may find this difficult at first.

Solving problems

What shall I do? How shall I do it?

- **Ask** – your teacher.
- **Ask** – your friends.
- **Ask** – other people.

I need some information, but I don't know where to find it.

- Read pages 3 and 4 of the Toolkit.
- Try asking people (see above).
- Look in the library or learning centre.

I don't understand the book I'm reading.

- See if someone else can explain it to you.
- See if you can find another book which is easier to read.
- Do you need to read the book? Perhaps you can find another way of getting the information. Try a CD-ROM or a newspaper.
- See if you can find another book which you feel explains things more clearly.

I've found a book that helps, but I can't find the piece of information I'm looking for.

- Try the contents pages at the front of the book. The chapter headings may help you.
- Look at the index at the back of the book.

The computer won't do what I want.

- See if there's a manual or a worksheet you can use.
- Find 'Help' on the menu and see if that gives you some ideas.
- Is there anyone else in the room who knows what to do?

I've got to interview someone and I'm nervous.

- Write out an interview plan in advance.
- Make sure you have a firm appointment.
- Take a friend with you, if possible.

I've got to give a presentation and I'm worried about it.

- Read pages 7 and 8 of the Toolkit.
- Be well prepared.
- Don't let your friends in the audience put you off or make you giggle.

I've got to phone an organisation.

○ Say who you are and who you want to talk to.

○ Know exactly what you want to ask.

○ Say thank-you and goodbye at the end of the conversation.

I've got to write a formal letter.

○ Check that you know the correct way to lay out a formal letter.

○ Always word process it, and use the spell check before printing.

○ Use headed paper, or make sure that your name and address are on the letter.

I don't enjoy writing reports and assignments.

○ Ask if you can give a presentation instead.

○ Talk to your tutor about how you feel and what you can do about it.

○ Think about why you don't like writing. Do you need some help with spelling, or putting your thoughts into words? Are you really unhappy about your handwriting? Can you use a word processor? Tackle a small part of your report or assignment at a time.

I'm not very good at spelling.

○ If you word process your work, spell check **everything**.

○ Ask a friend or tutor to read your work and point out mistakes, or use a dictionary to check it for yourself.

○ Ask your tutor if you can have extra help.

Carrying out research

You might wonder where to find the information you need to complete work for your GNVQ. Here are some suggestions.

○ If you want to find out about caring services in your area, try looking in the *Yellow Pages* or *Thomson Local Directory*. You could also try your doctor's surgery, a chemist shop, a supermarket or a health promotion unit.

○ **Books** are a good way to find information. You don't have to read a whole textbook to find what you're looking for. Try reading the **list of contents** to see if the chapter headings tell you where to look. If not, then most books have an **index** at the back of the book. Look up a word in the index (for instance, you could look up 'mobility') and if the book deals with that topic you should find the number of one or more pages on which there is information.

● If the books in your own library do not have the information you need, try your local **public library**. Librarians will be able to help you find different books and other sources of information on the subjects you're interested in. For instance, most libraries now have a CD-ROM available. You'll find that there are whole encyclopaedias available on CD-ROM, with pictures and photographs which you can print out for your portfolio. Libraries have copies of the **electoral register** for your area. This is very useful if you need information like how many houses or flats there are with only one person living in them, or how many houses or flats there are in a certain street or area. Most libraries will also have copies of

laws and **acts** which affect health and social care. You may not be able to take these away, but you will be able to read them in the library.

● You could try asking questions of the relevant departments of your local council, such as **Social Services, Community Service** and **Housing. Health Centres**, **police stations** and the officer of the **Department of Social Security** may also be able to help. Remember that the people who work in these places are all very busy, and you will need to make an appointment if you want to interview them. (Leaflets from these places will be a lot easier to get than interviews, and they will give you a lot of valuable information!)

Writing questionnaires

Questionnaires can be a good way to find out information, but watch out! It's easy to write questionnaires that don't find out the information you really want. For your questionnaires at Foundation level, try following these simple rules.

● Keep your questionnaire short.

● Make sure that you ask for **all** the information you need. Compare your questionnaire with an outline of what you want to find out.

● Lay out your questionnaire so it is easy to read.

● Decide whether you're going to put your questions face to face, or give people a questionnaire form to fill in.

● Test your questionnaire on a small group of people before you use it.

● Rewrite any questions they don't understand.

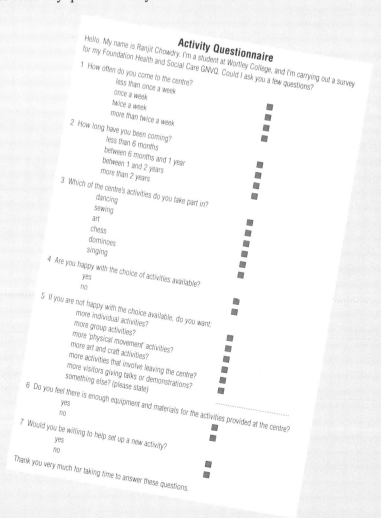

Activity Questionnaire

Hello. My name is Ranjit Chowdry. I'm a student at Wortley College, and I'm carrying out a survey for my Foundation Health and Social Care GNVQ. Could I ask you a few questions?

1 How often do you come to the centre?
    less than once a week
    once a week
    twice a week
    more than twice a week

2 How long have you been coming?
    less than 6 months
    between 6 months and 1 year
    between 1 and 2 years
    more than 2 years

3 Which of the centre's activities do you take part in?
    dancing
    sewing
    art
    chess
    dominoes
    singing

4 Are you happy with the choice of activities available?
    yes
    no

5 If you are not happy with the choice available, do you want:
    more individual activities?
    more group activities?
    more 'physical movement' activities?
    more art and craft activities?
    more activities that involve leaving the centre?
    more visitors giving talks or demonstrations?
    something else? (please state)

6 Do you feel there is enough equipment and materials for the activities provided at the centre?
    yes
    no

7 Would you be willing to help set up a new activity?
    yes
    no

Thank you very much for taking time to answer these questions.

Health and safety

Health and safety is an important part of everyone's working life. If your job involves you in any dangerous activity, then it is the law that your employer provides you with safety equipment. For instance, if your job involves contact with body fluids, e.g blood, you should be given a supply of rubber gloves to protect you and your client from the possibility of infection.

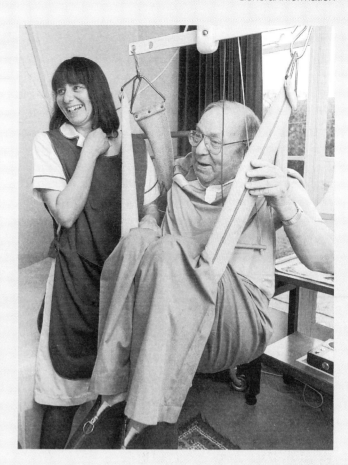

Trade Unions often bring health and safety issues to the attention of an organisation's management. However, there is a law which gives clear directions on what an organisation must do to make sure that its employees are safe and well.

This is called the **Health and Safety at Work Act 1974** (the date is different if you live in Northern Ireland).

- The Act covers all places of work, including factories, shops, farms, colleges and schools.
- If there is a recognised trade union, it should appoint someone to be the employee's safety representative, who will try to make sure that the Act is carried out.
- Employers must make the place of work as safe as possible, and supply safety equipment where necessary.
- There are particular rules about handling dangerous substances.
- It is the responsibility of both employers and employees to make sure that working practices are safe.

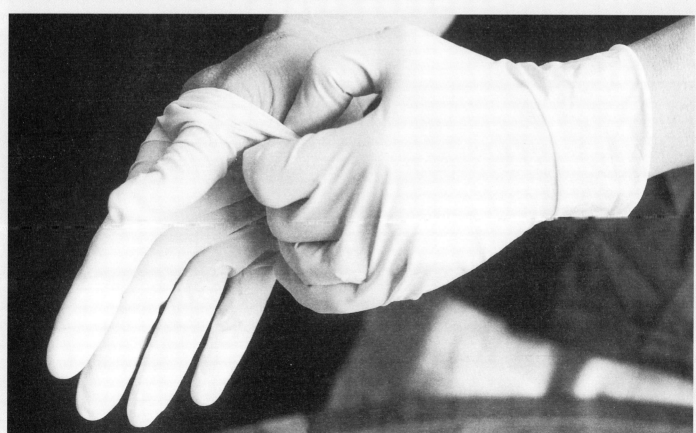

Communication

Good communication skills are very important for working in health and social care. You will need to be able to talk with and write to a wide range of people in many different ways.

For instance, you will need to talk to people on the telephone, in meetings and during interviews. Caring is very much about communicating with clients and forming relationships which support them, so you will need to be a good listener as well as good at talking.

Listening skills

The setting

If you can, make sure that the setting for an interview or discussion is as good as possible:

● choose a place offering some privacy – even if it is only the quietest corner of a busy room
● avoid distractions like rattling window blinds or a flickering light
● remove barriers such as large desks or tables
● create comfort to try to put the other person at ease. Sit in armchairs of a similar height and provide coffee.

Your body language

Be an active listener:

look at the person who is talking

nod and smile when you agree

use other facial expressions as appropriate to show you are registering what is being said

face the person who is talking

make eye-contact but don't stare

lean forward slightly in your chair to show you are interested

avoid building barriers of crossed arms and legs.

Your voice

Help the other person talk:

● make sure your voice sounds interested
● ask questions – it helps others to focus their thoughts
● give appropriate prompts – 'uh-huh', 'go on', 'mmm', 'really?'

 For more on body language, see page 9.

Talking skills

People who work in health and social care need to talk to a wide range of people on different subjects.

Talking on the telephone

Remember: no one can see you smile or frown over the telephone, so make sure your voice and the words you use send clear messages.

Preparing for the call

1 Get a pen and paper so you can make notes.
2 Check that you have the phone number and extension.
3 Check the name and job title of the person you're calling.
4 Prepare a list of questions to ask.
5 Decide what information you want them to provide.
6 Make sure you know your number in case they need to return your call.
7 Check that you know your address – including the postcode – for any written reply.

The call itself

1 Give your name, and explain briefly why you are calling.
2 Give the name and job title of the person to whom you wish to speak.
3 Repeat **(1)** if necessary. When you ring an organisation, the call will often need to be transferred – make sure you don't off-load all your questions or information on the wrong person.
4 Ask your questions and/or give your information.
5 Speak clearly and avoid using slang.
6 Give the other person time to think, reply and/or take notes.
7 Where appropriate, show you are listening by saying 'uh-huh', 'yes, I see', and so on.
8 Make a note of important details (for example, names, addresses, ages and dates) and run though them at the end of the conversation to make sure you wrote them down correctly.
9 Give your details so you can be contacted by telephone or post.
10 Finish the call appropriately (for example, say 'thanks' or 'look forward to seeing you on Friday'), using the other person's name if possible.

Making presentations

Much of the work you carry out for your GNVQ, and many of the activities in this book, ask you to make oral presentations. You need certain skills to give a good presentation, and this section will help you.

Preparing the room

When you are going to make a presentation, get to the room early (before your audience) so that you can check everything is ready.

Run through the following checklist.

● Is the room set out the way you want?
● Are there enough chairs? Too many chairs?

● Can everyone see the overhead projector (OHP)?
● Is the OHP working?
● Is there a table for you?
● Do you need marker pens and a board cleaner? If so, have you got them?

Preparing yourself

You do not want to distract your audience from what you are telling them. Wear clothes you find comfortable which also suit the occasion and the subject. Clothes just a little more formal than your usual ones will encourage your audience to take your presentation seriously.

Stand up straight and look at your audience. It can be difficult to hear someone who is looking down all the time. Try it with your friends and see how quickly your voice is lost if you look down.

Planning what to say

Your presentation needs a clear structure. Start by telling people what you are going to talk about, and for how long. Tell them whether you want them to ask questions as you go along or at the end. If your presentation is to last longer than about five minutes, add a timetable to your plan.

Getting your message across

You should speak very clearly, and loudly enough for the people at the back of the room to hear you. Reading from notes muffles your voice and limits eye contact, so make sure you know what you are going to say in advance. If you want something to remind you, write key words or sentences on small cards and keep them next to you.

Practise your presentation before you actually give it. Try timing your talk as well – sometimes it's surprising how long or short a time it takes. If you practise in front of a mirror, you will get an idea of what the audience will see. This may help you avoid fidgeting, using mannerisms, or doing things that will stop your audience concentrating on what you are saying.

Try to give your audience something to look at. Overhead transparencies are a good idea, as you can prepare them in advance. If you use overhead transparency pens, avoid red and green – they are difficult to see. If there isn't an overhead projector, write on the whiteboard or blackboard. Or you may be able to borrow a flip chart with large sheets of paper. Again, practise in advance to make sure that you make your letters large enough for everyone to see, and spell all the words correctly.

Body language

Body language is the term used for the ways our bodies send messages – messages which may make people believe, or not believe, what our words are saying.

The body can send messages in many ways; for example, through:

- the eyes – making eye contact shows the person you're talking to that you're listening
- the face – your facial expression can show your attitude to an idea, argument or suggestion
- gestures with the head, arms and legs, and hands – to show agreement or disagreement, anger or calm, certainty or doubt, enthusiasm or boredom. For example, folding your arms can hold people at a distance, while opening your arms can show welcome
- posture – for example, leaning forward shows you're interested
- position in relation to others – for example, sitting close to people can show that you're comfortable with their views or feelings.

With experience, body language can be a useful way to make your views clear. But take care your body doesn't tell a story you don't want told.

Writing skills

It's not always possible, or convenient, to explain something to someone face-to-face or over the telephone. If this is the case, you need to write a letter.

Reference number – if there is one, quote the reference number from their letter to you and give them yours. This can help with filing and finding letters.

Your address – should be clear and written in full (include your postcode, and write 'Road', not 'Rd').

Date of writing in full, including the word for the month, in the order day-month-year.

Recipient's name and address – to make it clear who you are sending the letter to.

Greeting – 'Dear ...'. Use the person's name if possible.

Introductory sentence or paragraph – should expand on the title and prepare the reader for the rest of the letter.

Title – a short heading that explains what the letter's about.

Body of the letter – the main points with details. The number of paragraphs you include will depend on how complicated the subject is.

Concluding paragraph – this may be a single sentence that sums up what you will do, or would like the other person to do.

Subscription – a polite, formal phrase before the signature. If the letter is written to a named person, use 'Yours sincerely'. Otherwise, write 'Yours faithfully'.

Signature – even if this is legible, you should print your name underneath.

Gladleigh Day Centre
Hadlam Street
Rainford
Surrey GU14 6QT

17 November 1996

Ref: CA/V/S

Ms Jane Somerton
15 Bankside Terrace
Rainford
Surrey GU14 5BG

Dear Ms Somerton

Christmas Pantomime

Thank you very much for your letter dated 13th November. The offer you made on behalf of your amateur drama group, 'Age Link', to present a pantomime for our members, is very kind. I hope we shall be able to enjoy your version of 'Sleeping Beauty' in the week beginning 11th December, as you suggest.

However, I think it is very important that you visit us soon. You can have a careful look at our facilities and meet some of our members. We can also discuss matters such as insurance. (Could you telephone me between the hours of 8.30 a.m. and 4 p.m., in the next day or two, so we can arrange an early visit?

Thank you once again, and I look forward to meeting you soon.

Yours sincerely,

Balbir Kaur

Balbir Kaur
Centre Manager

Collect a range of formal letters to compare them. If you think any of the information in them might be private, blank it out so that colleagues, tutors and others cannot read it.

Memoranda (memos)

The memorandum (shortened to 'memo' by most people) is a way to communicate quickly and easily within organisations.

For example, on the 18th March, 1996, Mrs Willis, Care Manager at Golden Park Home, sent this memo to her deputy, Ms Wilma Jenkins, who was taking her weekly day off.

GOLDEN PARK HOME

internal memorandum

From: Shelia Willis   Date: 18.5.96
To: Wilma Jenkins
Subject: Code of Practice: Privacy

Today I received a complaint that a new member of our staff entered a resident's room without knocking. This caused the resident some embarrassment and the care assistant failed to offer an apology. I shall speak to the care assistant myself during the day. Please arrange to meet with me for half-an-hour tomorrow morning at 10.00 so we can discuss this incident and review our arrangements for training new staff.

S.W.

The headed memo form shows that it is an internal memo.

The form prompts Mrs Willis to supply basic information: from whom, to whom, when, about what. This provides a record for filing.

The blank memo has enough space for a short message. It encourages people to be brief, and give the facts in plain language and simple style.

Initialling the memo gives a personal touch and confirms that it is genuine.

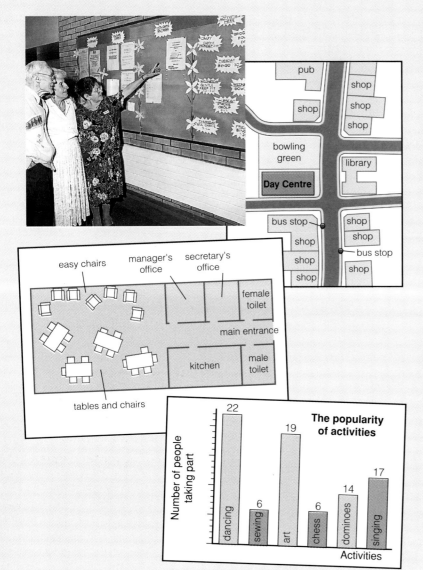

Using images

Images are pictures – such as bar charts, flow charts, pictograms, spider diagrams and photographs – which can help make written communication clearer.

Helpful hints

● Don't use images just to make your work prettier – use them to help you communicate. Make sure that the image you use is appropriate – you might be tempted to use a striking image when it's not actually relevant.

● Whenever you make an important point in writing or speech, ask yourself whether you could make your point clearer by including an image.

Simple reports

Your reports shouldn't be mystery tours with surprising endings – they should follow clear, easy-to-follow paths, pointing to the end from the start. Try using the following structure for your reports.

● Title page, including the report title, your name and date.

● Terms of reference – what you were asked to do. Include this so you can refer back to it when writing your conclusions.

● Methods used – reading, observing, interviewing and so on.

● Findings – the facts, figures and views. You might present these in a variety of ways, including graphs and pictograms.

● Conclusions – what do your findings tell you? For instance, if you interviewed elderly people and found that the majority worried about security in their home you might conclude that a council programme to fit door chains and improved locks would be popular.

● Sources – include a list of the books and periodicals you referred to, and the people and organisations you talked to. Arrange them in sections, in alphabetical order.

Use words you're sure you understand and write in a straightforward style. You are usually expected to be impersonal. For instance, a report on homelessness in your area might record:

'Sixty people were interviewed on their attitude to homelessness. Twenty were full-time students; twenty were employed people; twenty were unemployed. Only fifteen thought that homeless people were themselves to blame for their situation.'

You should **not**, in a report, say:

'As you might guess, employed people take an 'I'm all right' attitude.

Application of Number and Information Technology

As well as being able to communicate well with people, you need to be able to use numbers and computers when working in business. This is why Foundation Health & Social Care GNVQ includes core skills units in Application of Number (maths) and Information Technology (using computers).

This section includes some information, advice and activities which might help you on your way.

Percentages

It is very important to remember that a **percentage** is just a particular type of fraction.

ninths $\frac{75}{99}$ quarters $\frac{27}{39}$

$\frac{135}{367}$ tenths $\frac{200}{365}$ $3/7$

half

$3.04 = 3\frac{4}{100}$ $0.78 = \frac{78}{100}$

- **Fractions** can have **any** whole number as a **denominator** (bottom number). This means there are many different types of **fraction**.

- **Decimal fractions** can only have powers of **10** as denominators (tenths, hundredths, thousandths and so on), so we can put them in columns to match whole numbers. We use the decimal point to show where the whole numbers stop and the fractions start.

- Percentages are fractions out of 100.
- Per cent means 'for each hundred' or 'out of a hundred'.

We use a special sign as a quick way of writing per cent – %. This means the same as 100.

So

$7\% = \frac{7}{100}$ $26\% = \frac{26}{100}$ $100\% = \frac{100}{100} = 1$

Watch out! 100% does not mean 100.

To use a percentage we need to write it as a fraction.

Example

To find 6% of £40, change 6% to its fraction form and multiply by £40.

$6\% \text{ of } £40 = \frac{6}{100} \times 40 = £2.40$

Using a calculator:

`6 ÷ 1 0 0 x 4 0 = 2 . 4`

We write money with **two** numbers after the decimal point to represent the pence, so 2.4 becomes £2.40.

VAT

In business, people often need to work out VAT (Value Added Tax) which is given as a percentage.

Example

If you need to add VAT to £65 and the rate of VAT is 17.5%, change 17.5% to its fraction form then multiply by £65.

$$17.5\% \text{ of } £65 = \frac{17.5}{100} \times 65 = £11.375 = £11.38$$

Using a calculator:

$$17.5 \div 100 \times 65 = 11.375$$

This gives you too many decimal places, so you need to **round** the answer to the nearest penny, giving you £11.38.

This is the amount of VAT. Add this to the original price to get the total:

$$£65 + VAT = £65 + £11.38 = £76.38$$

Rounding numbers

● If a decimal is exactly halfway (or more than halfway) between two numbers you should round it up to the next penny. So £11.375 becomes £11.38

● If a decimal is less than halfway between two numbers you should round it down to the penny below. So £6.342 becomes £6.34.

Discounts

Finding a 20% discount means we find 20% then take the answer away from the original amount.

Example

Millfield Nursery wish to buy the tricycle costing £55 with a 20% discount.
Find the discount and the sale price of the tricycle.

$$20\% \text{ of } £55 = \frac{20}{100} \times 55 = £11$$

Calculator: $20 \div 100 \times 55 = 11$
Now take the £11 from the original price of £55
Sale price = £55 − £11 = £44.

Activity
Using percentages

1 **a** Millfield Nursery buy a computer for £950 plus VAT (at 17.5%). How much VAT do they have to pay?

   b What is the total price of the computer?

2 Jan gets a bill for herself and her friend's meal which reads £36.40. The restaurant adds a further 10% for service. What is the total bill including service?

3 **a** Mrs Singh is to pay £420 for her holiday; because she is over 65 years old she is allowed a 5% reduction. How much would this reduction be?

   b How much does she have to pay for her holiday?

4 A children's slide is marked '10% OFF MARKED PRICE'. If the marked price is £158.90, what is the reduced price?

5 A primary school served 820 meals in the first week in January. In the following week many of the children had flu and the number of meals dropped by 15%. How many meals were served during the second week?

6 Complete the following invoice

Invoice No.			Unit price	Total price
Quantity	Description		£0.00	£0.00
			123.49	£
2	M-1475 Mattresses		11.99	£
4	M-1476 Fitted sheets			
			Total cost	£
			Discount 10%	£
			Sub total	£
			Add VAT 17.5%	£
			Net payable	£

See page 29 for the answers.

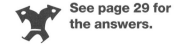

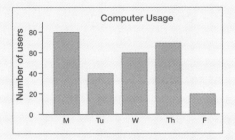

Computer Usage

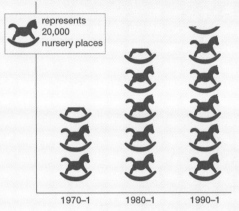

Nursery places in the Public Sector

Pictorial presentation

It is often useful to include graphs and charts in your work. They can give a good picture of data, making it easier to see the general result. Remember, because they are pictures they often do not provide detailed information. For detail, you should look at the original information.

During your GNVQ you will use:

Bar charts

● each bar is the same width
● each bar should be labelled
● the height of the bar shows 'how many' – the frequency
● one axis has a scale; the other has labels
● bar charts can be horizontal or vertical

Pictograms

● also known as pictographs
● use symbols (pictures) rather than bars
● all pictures should be the same size
● pictures are chosen to emphasise the topic

Bar charts

Bar charts, or graphs, can be drawn with the bars horizontal or with the bars vertical. Vertical bar charts are the most common.

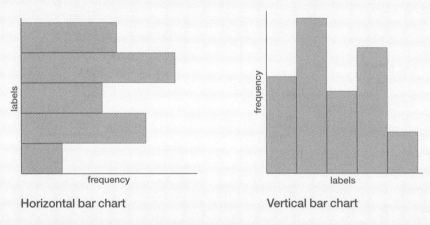

Horizontal bar chart

Vertical bar chart

The axis for frequency must be to **scale** – evenly spaced. The main decision you have to make is **what scale to use**.

Each square must be worth the **same amount**.

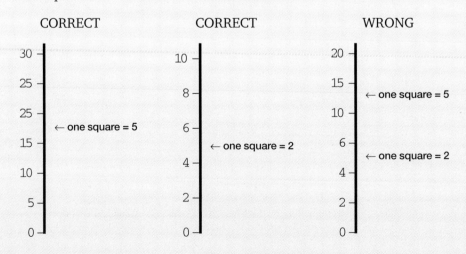

You need to look at the frequency information and the number of squares on your graph paper. Choose a scale to make sure the frequency makes the best fit to the paper. Be careful not to choose an awkward scale – keep to 2s, 5s, 10s, 20s, 100s avoid 3s and other awkward numbers.

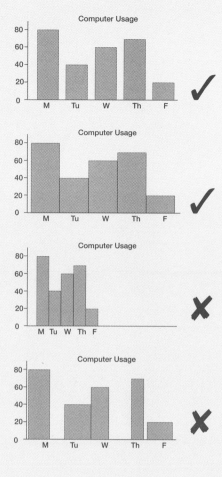

> **Examples** using a sheet of graph paper 30 cm long

1 Fit a frequency of up to 50

Best fit is 2 per cm giving a frequency of up to 60.

2 Fit a frequency of up to 100

Could use 4 per cm but this can be awkward – best fit would then be 5 per cm giving a maximum of 150

3 Fit a frequency of up to 550

Best fit is 20 per cm giving a maximum of 600

Drawing a bar chart

Having decided on the scale for your frequency, you need to draw bars to the correct height. Make sure you understand the meaning of your scale and the smaller parts of it; for example, what does 0.5 cm show on your graph?

Each bar must be the same width. You can leave gaps between the bars if you wish, or you can keep them next to each other. Make the graph fit on the page and give it a title.

The height of each bar should match its 'frequency' (how many times it occurs). There is no need to put the bars in order of size.

Reading a bar chart

Having drawn the graph, you can use it to find out information.

> **Example**

Millfield nursery records the height of each of their fifty children.

A bar chart for the same information might look like this:

Height in cm	Number of children
96	3
97	9
98	9
99	8
100	10
101	7
102	4

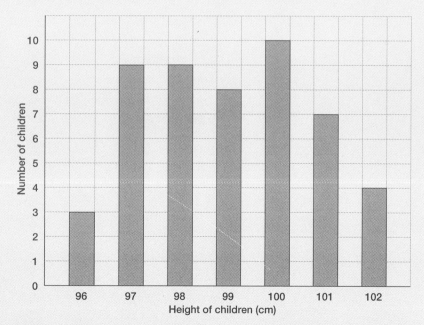

Which height occurs most often?
What is the smallest height in this group?
What is the tallest height in this group?
What is the difference in height between the tallest and the smallest children?

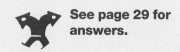

See page 29 for answers.

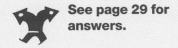

See page 29 for answers.

Activity Barcharts

Dr Kingston recorded how many patients (to the nearest ten) attend the Accident and Emergency unit at her local hospital.

Day	Sun	Mon	Tues	Wed	Thurs	Fri	Sat
Patients	30	50	25	65	50	90	115

Use squared paper to draw a bar chart showing the number of patients.
From the graph state:

1 which day had most patients; why do you think this might be?
2 which day had the least patients
3 which two days had the same number of patients.

Pictograms

Pictograms are graphs which use pictures to make a point clearly.
For example:

● if your topic is cigarette smoking, you might use pictures of cigarettes
● if your topic is the number killed in a war, you might use pictures of crosses or coffins
● if your topic is traffic, you might use pictures of cars, lorries or buses.

Note: even if you use different pictures in the same graph, each picture must be the same size.

To save time and effort we usually let each picture represent more than 1.
For example:

might represent 200 buses

might represent less than 200 buses

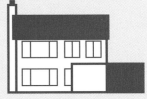

might represent 1000 houses

One of the problems with pictograms is that it is difficult to show the difference between similar numbers, for example 691 buses. You could show part of a bus to show less than 200 buses but you couldn't show detailed differences.

Example

This is a pictogram to show the increase in the number of nursery places in the public sector from 1970 to 1990.
It does not need to show exactly how many places there were each year, the important issue is the **increase**.

This pictogram shows that the number of nursery places in the public sector is increasing. We can also see that the number increased more in the first ten years than the second ten years.

Note: We are not sure just how many the 'part rocking horse' represents.

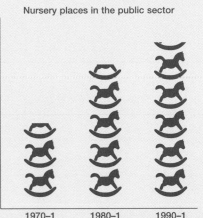

Nursery places in the public sector

1970–1   1980–1   1990–1

represents 20,000 nursery places

Activity
Using pictograms

1 Information from *Social Trends* about the number of people in the UK who had measles between 1987 and 1992 is rounded to the nearest thousand as follows:

1987	46000
1988	91000
1989	31000
1990	16000
1991	12000
1992	12000

A medical researcher produces a report to show how the number of cases was going down. Draw a pictogram as part of this report. Use one sad face to represent 10,000 people.

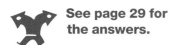 **See page 29 for the answers.**

2 Population

The council of Little Village drew this pictogram to show how the population of the village was growing.

Use the pictogram to answer the following questions:

a Approximately, what was the population of Little Village in 1950?

b Approximately what was the increase in the population between 1950 and 1990?

c Approximately, what was the population of Little Village in 1990?

d How will services in this village change as the population increases?

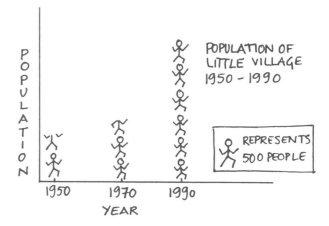

Measure

In Britain, we currently use two systems of measurement – the Imperial System and the Metric System.

Systems of measurement

The Imperial System has been used in Britain for many years. It includes different systems for **weight**, **length** and **capacity** (measuring liquids and volumes) developed a long time ago. For example, the measurement of one foot was abut the length of a man's foot, and a yard about one stride! We still use some of these measures, even though we have 'gone metric'.

The **Metric System** was introduced in Britain fairly recently. It is widely used in the rest of Europe. Each metric measure uses a number system based on **thousands**. There is a base unit for each type of measurement (the metre for length, the gram for weight, and the litre for capacity). Each of these can be broken down into 1000 small pieces (millimetres, milligrams and millilitres), or 1000 can be joined together to make a larger measurement (kilometre, kilogram and kilolitre). Because the millimetre (mm) and millilitre (ml) are very small, we also use the centimetre (10 mm) and the centilitre (10 ml).

The metric system was designed to link different units:

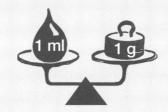

1 cubic centimetre of water has a volume of 1 millilitre and weighs 1 gram

Which is measured using the Metric System – beer or wine?

Beer is measured in pints

Wine is measure in centilitres

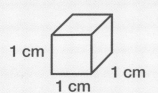

Look out for imperial and metric measures in shops:

What is the normal weight of a bag of sugar or a bag of flour?

How do you buy your milk?

Would you ask your grocer for a pound of apples or a kilo of apples?

Do we buy petrol by the litre or by the gallon?

Metric and Imperial

The Imperial System

Length
12 inches = 1 foot (12" = 1')

3 feet = 1 yard (3' = 1 yd)

1760 yards = 1 mile

Weight
16 ounces = 1 pound (16 oz = 1 lb)

14 pounds = 1 stone (14 lb = 1 st)

112 pounds = 1 hundredweight (112 lb = 1 cwt)

20 hundredweight = 1 ton (20 cwt = 1 t)

Capacity
20 fluid ounces = 1 pint (20 fl oz = 1 pt)

2 pints = 1 quart (2 pt = 1 qt)

8 pints = 1 gallon (8 pt = 1 gal)

Temperature
Measured in degrees Fahrenheit (°F)

Water freezes at 32°F

Water boils at 212°F

The Metric System

Length
1000 millimetres = 1 metre

(1000 mm = 1 m)

1000 metres = 1 kilometre

(1000 m = 1 km)

10 millimetres = 1 centimetre

(10 mm = 1 cm)

100 centimetres = 1 metre

(100 cm = 1 m)

Weight
1000 milligrams = 1 gram

(1000 mg = 1 g)

1000 grams = 1 kilogram

(1000g = 1 kg)

1000 kilograms = 1 tonne

(1000 kg = 1 t)

Capacity
1000 millilitres = 1 litre

(1000 ml = 1 l)

(the kilolitre is not often used)

10 millilitres = 1 centilitre

(10 ml = 1 cl)

100 centilitres = 1 litres

(100 cl = 1 l)

Temperature
Measured in degrees Celsius or Centigrade (°C)

Water freezes at 0°C

Water boils at 100°C

Changing between metric and Imperial

Approximately:
- 2.5 cm = 1 inch
- 30 cm = 1 foot
- 1 metre = 39 inches
  = 1 yard 3 inches
- 8 kilometres = 5 miles
- 1 kilogram = 2.2 pounds (lb)
- 1 litre = 1.75 pints

To change:
- °F to °C, subtract 32, multiply by 5 and divide by 9
- °C to °F, multiply by 9, divide by 5, and add 32.

Paper

Nurseries, schools etc. use a great deal of paper. Most will be standard 'International Paper Size' – the most common is called the 'A' Series.

This includes:

- A0 paper, which has an area of 1 square metre. It measures 841 mm × 1189 mm (to the nearest millimetre)
- A1 paper, which is half the size of A0
- A2 paper, which is half the size of A1; and so on.

The diagram below shows the relative sizes of paper from A0 down to A6 size, although there are also smaller sizes. probably the most common size for letters is A4, which measures 210 mm x 297 mm.

Paper is usually bought in reams (500 sheets) or quires (25 sheets).

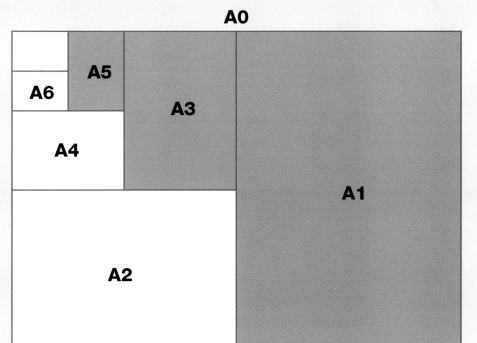

	Size in mm
A0	841 × 1189
A1	594 × 841
A2	420 × 594
A3	297 × 420
A4	210 × 297
A5	148 × 210
A6	105 × 148
A7	74 × 105
A8	52 × 74
A9	37 × 52

Activity
Using measurements

Millfield Council are drawing up plans for a home for the elderly. Some of these elderly people will be in wheelchairs so they need to make sure that all their rooms will be big enough. The plans make each room 4 metres long, 3 metres wide and 2.5 metres high; each will have a window 1.5 metres high and 1 metre wide in the middle of a narrow wall and a door 2 metres high by 1 metre wide on the opposite wall.

They plan to put in (floor space needed in brackets))

● a bed (1 metre by 2 metres)
● a wardrobe (1 metre wide, 50 cm deep)
● a chest of drawers (1 metre wide, 50 cm deep)
● a table (50 cm by 50 cm)
● a comfortable chair (60 cm by 60 cm)

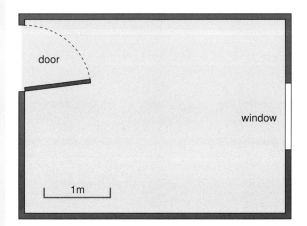

You have been asked to

a find out how big a wheelchair is and how much space it needs to turn around

b plan the room to show where the furniture should go

c draw a scale plan of the room with the furniture and decide if the room will be big enough

d find the cost of painting the walls and adding a decorative border around the walls

e find the cost of putting in a fitted carpet

You have been given the following additional information: the Council can buy

● emulsion paint for 80p per litre

● carpet for £5.90 per square metre from a roll which is 4 metres wide

● underlay for the carpet for £1.50 per square metre (roll is 4 metres wide)

● decorative borders for £3.50 a roll (10 metres long).

There should be two coats of emulsion paint and the first coat of emulsion paint should be diluted at a rate of 2:1 (2 parts paint to one part water)

area = length × width

Conversion

If you need to change from one unit of measurement to another (for example, from litres to gallons), you can use:

- a conversion factor
- a conversion table
- a conversion chart or graph.

Conversion factors

A conversion factor is useful if we only have one or two calculations to do and we are not going to need to do them very often. If we use a conversion factor we can be as accurate as we want to be.

> **Example**

The conversion factor to change pounds to kilograms is 0.4536
The conversion factor to change kilograms to pounds is 2.2046
This means that **one pound is 0.4536 kilograms** and there are **2.2046 pounds in one kilogram**.

To change pounds to kilograms we need to multiply by 0.4536.
To change kilograms to pounds we multiply by 2.2046.

If a baby is born weighing 3.2 kilograms the mother may want to know what this is in pounds. To change the kilograms to pounds multiply by 2.2046. This gives 7.05472. The mother does not need this degree of accuracy.

In a maternity ward the midwives may need to work this out quite often. They may choose to use a conversion table or a conversion graph/chart.

Conversion tables

A conversion table might look something like this:

We work out each conversion once – using the rules above and put the answers in a table. Now we can read the table instead of working the answers out each time.

Kilograms		Pounds
0.454	1	2.204
0.907	2	4.409
1.361	3	6.614
1.814	4	8.818
2.268	5	11.023

You can either

read the centre column as kilograms and the right hand column as pounds
  or
read the centre column as pounds and the left hand column as kilograms

The conversion table can be designed to go as high as you think might be needed – do we need to convert 100 pounds to kilograms?

Each of the numbers in the table can be rounded to the degree of accuracy we need e.g.

1 kilogram = 2.204 pounds = 2.2 pounds

However, a conversion table does not always answer all our problems – can we use this table to change 3.5 kilograms to pounds?

Conversion graphs

Sometimes it is useful to draw a conversion graph. We use the answers we have already worked out. We plot three useful points on a graph.

We join these points together to give a straight line.

We can then read all other conversions from this graph.

0 kilograms = 0 pounds

5 kilograms = 11 pounds

10 kilograms = 22 pounds

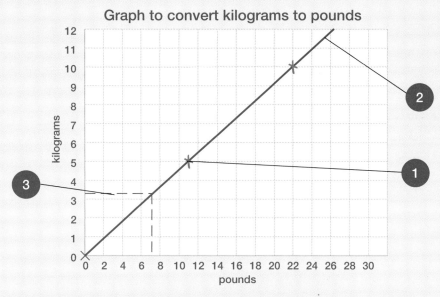

Graph to convert kilograms to pounds

1   X marks the plotted points. These were joined together to give the straight line.

2   Notice that the line does not stop at the last point, but goes to the end of the graph.

3   The dotted line shows that 3.3 kilograms is approximately 7 pounds.

A conversion graph is often not as accurate as using a conversion factor or conversion table (using the conversion factor 3.3 kilograms = 7.05472 pounds) but it is a quick and often easy way to change between units.

 Activity
Conversion graphs

See page 29 for the answers.

1   Draw the graph converting kilograms to pounds for yourself. Use your graph to find out

i   how many pounds in 9 kilograms?

ii   how many kilograms in 14 pounds?

iii   A baby girl weighed 2.5 kilograms at birth. When her parents later weighed her as a toddler she weighed 19 pounds. What weight had she put on?

a   in pounds?

b   in kilograms?

2   Steven uses his mother's old recipe book which only shows measures in pounds and ounces (oz).

He has a new set of metric scales weighing grams and kilograms.

He decides to draw a conversion chart to help him convert his recipes.

He knows

ounces	grams
0	0
8	227
16	454

Use these values to draw Steven's conversion chart.

Use it to convert this recipe for fruit cake:

He has to round each amount to the nearest 5 grams as this is the smallest weight he has.

Fruit Cake

6 oz butter
6 oz sugar
4 eggs
8 oz plain flour
pinch salt
8 oz sultanas
6 oz currants
2 oz cherries

Using information technology

Computers are very good at dealing with numbers and producing graphs. It is important that we know how to produce graphs by hand, but a large care organisation would always use IT to produce well-finished graphs or charts.

To produce a graph or chart on the computer, you have to begin with a spreadsheet or database.

Using a spreadsheet

The following information is generally true, but you must learn how to use the spreadsheet package you have at school or college as they are all slightly different.

The information is put into a table.

Sophie collected information about the number of kilocalories (kcals) and the number of grams of fat there were in 100 grams of certain things she liked to eat. She chose chocolate, bread, low fat spread, baked beans and crisps. She recorded the information in a table like this:

	A	B	C	D
	GNUQ Worksheet (SS)			
A1	× ✓ Item			
1	Item	kcals	fat	
2	Chocolate	529	30	
3	Bread	235	2	
4	Low fat spread	364	39	
5	Baked beans	100	0.5	
6	Crisps	546	38	
7				
8				

Each piece of information is placed in a cell, described using a letter at the top of the column and the number at the beginning of the row. This means the word 'Item' is in cell A1. The number 529 is in the cell B2.

Producing graphs

By using the graph option in the spreadsheet or database you can produce graphs like these:

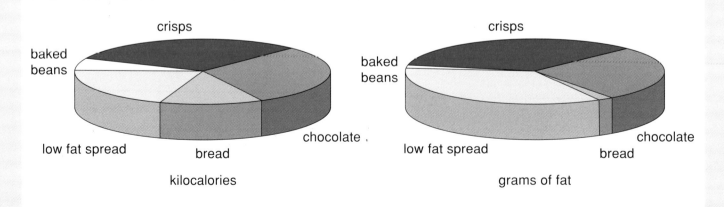

kilocalories   grams of fat

Graphs to show total number of kilocalories and number of kilocalories from fat:

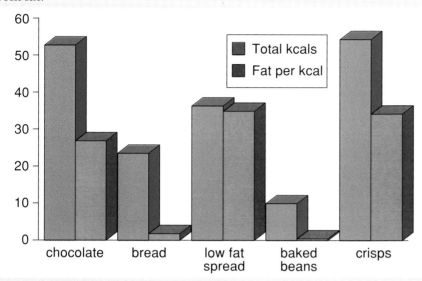

For the bar chart the information was changed. The number of grams of fat was changed to the number of kilocalories from this fat using the fact that there are 9 kcals in each 1 gram of fat. This could be done using a calculator and inputting the answers but we can use the power of the spreadsheet and put in a formula.

 ## Activity Spreadsheets

Find out how to put a formula into the spreadsheet you are using (this often starts with + or =)

Step 1 – find the number of kcals in 30 g of fat (chocolate) and put the answer in cell D2.

Select D2 first, then put in your formula.

	A	B	C	D	E
	Item	kcals	fat		
2	chocolate	529	30	270	
3	bread	235	2		
4	low fat spread	364	39		
5	baked beans	100	0.5		
6	crisps	546	38		
7					
8					

D2 =C2*9

Your formula could look like this:

=C2*9

Notice we chose C2 rather than putting in 30 and we use * for multiply.

You should get 270 in D2.

Repeat this for each of the other items. Your spreadsheet should look like this:

	A	B	C	D	E
	Item	kcals	fat	fat kcals	
2	chocolate	529	30	270	
3	bread	235	2	18	
4	low fat spread	364	39	351	
5	baked beans	100	0.5	4.5	
6	crisps	546	38	342	
7					
8					

D6 =C6*9

We can also find what percentage of the total number of kilocalories are provided by the fat. We can put this in column E.

Step 2: What percentage of the kcals for chocolate come from fat

Select E2 (for the answer). Put in your formula.

=C2/B2*100

Notice we use / for divide and the cell names rather than the actual numbers.

You should get 51.0396975

Note: Use the format function to round all the answers to one decimal place so that the column does not get full of numbers like this.

Repeat this for the other items.

If we use this information we can see which items have the highest percentage of kilocalories from fat.

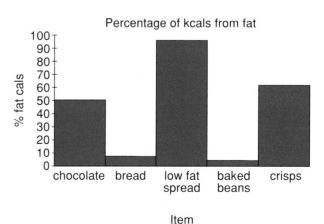

Percentage of kcals from fat

From this graph we can see that almost all the kilocalories in low fat spread come from fat whilst hardly any of the kcals in baked beans come from fat. If you want a low fat diet, baked beans and bread look all right but the other items provide too much fat.

Activity Foods

Choose some foods you eat every day. Make a list of about 8 to 10 items. Look at food tables or read the labels to find out the nutritional information for 100 grams of each item.

Find out how many kilocalories 100 grams of each food would provide and how many grams of fat and how many grams of protein each provides.

Put this information into a spreadsheet and produce a short report including graphs to show

● total kcals and kcals from fat
● total kcals and kcals from protein
● percentage of kcals from fat
● percentage of kcals from protein.

Explain which of the foods you chose would be 'good for you' and which might not be.

Explain why you think this.

Safety first!

It is important to take safety into account when using IT equipment. How would you do things differently to the person below?

The mean, the mode and the range

The mean

This is the best-known average, also known as the **arithmetic mean**.

To help you understand, imagine six people have money, as shown on the right.

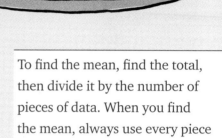

At the moment, the money isn't shared out equally – some people have more than others! Calculating the mean is like finding out how much each would have if the money was shared out equally. The total amount of money must stay the same.

To work this out they could put all their money on the table and then share it out. In our example, the total amount of money would be:

£6 + £5 + £3 + £2 + £1 + £1 = **£18**

Sharing this out equally between the six of them would give each one:

£18 ÷ 6 = **£3 each**

£3 is the mean.

To find the mean, find the total, then divide it by the number of pieces of data. When you find the mean, always use every piece of data.

Note:
● the mean doesn't have to be one of the original numbers
● the mean doesn't have to be a whole number – even when you're talking about people!

Example

To find the mean of £34, £56, £65, £72, £84:
● find the total – £34 + £65 + £65 + £72 + £84 = £311
● divide it by the number of pieces of data – £311 ÷ 5 = £62.2 = £62.20

The mode

This is the simplest average to 'work out'.

The mode is the most popular or most frequent figure – the value that crops up most often.

Example

If we look at the amounts of time in minutes 15 patients spent with the doctor in one day

6, 4, 4, 7, 4, 4, 6, 5, 4, 4, 6, 4, 5, 8, 4

We can draw up a **frequency table** – a table showing how many there are.

A quick way is to **tally** the data – for each number put a mark. To help keep track (especially for large numbers) we use a a '5-barred-gate' – the fifth mark is put across the other 4 to 'tie' them together.

For our numbers we get:

Data	Tally	Frequency
4	~~IIII~~ III	8
5	II	2
6	III	3
7	I	1
8	I	1

We can see that 8 patients spent 4 minutes with the doctor. We therefore say that the **modal time** was 4 minutes.

The range

The range of a set of numbers is the difference between the largest and the smallest.

For example, the range of 3, 8, 6, 9, 2, 7 = 9 – 2 = 7

To find the range of a set of numbers, simply look for the largest value and the smallest value, and work out the difference.

Example

If we look again at the amount of time 15 patients spent with the doctor

The range is 8 – 3 = 5, i.e. 5 minutes between the shortest and longest times

Activity
Mean, mode and range

The teachers in two classes asked each of their children how many brothers or sisters they had. These were the results they found:

	0	1	2	3	4
Class 4	6	10	6	2	1
Class 5	5	19	4	2	0

1 What is the modal number of brothers or sisters of the children in class 4?

2 What is the modal number of brothers or sisters of the children in class 5?

3 How many children were in class 4?

4 How many children were in class 5?

5 Calculate the mean number of brothers or sisters for the children in class 4. (You need to work out how many brothers or sisters they have altogether first.) What does this answer mean? Is it possible to have this number of brothers or sisters?

6 Repeat this for class 5. Compare your answer for class 5 with your answer for class 4. What do you find?

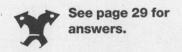
See page 29 for answers.

Answers

p.15 Activity Using percentages

1a £166.25

b £1116.25

2 £40.04

3a £21

b £399

4 £143.01

5 697 meals

6

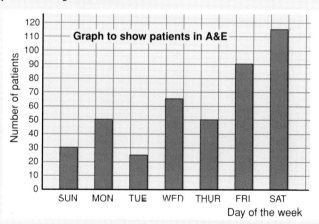

Invoice No.				
Quantity	Description		Unit price £0.00	Total price £0.00
2	M-1475 Mattresses		123.49	246.98
4	M-1476 Fitted sheets		11.99	47.96
		Total cost		294.94
		Discount 10%		29.49
		Sub total		265.45
		Add VAT 17.5%		46.45
		Net payable		219.00

p. 17 – Reading a bar chart

100 cm appears most often. Smallest is 96 cm. Tallest is 102 cm.

Difference between tallest and smallest is 6 cm.

p.18 – Days of the week

i Saturday – possibly because of sporting events.

ii Tuesday

iii Monday and Thursday

p.19 Activity

1

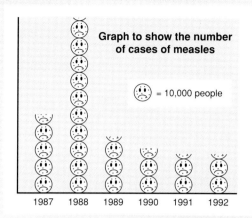

Graph to show the number of cases of measles

= 10,000 people

2 Population

a 750

b 1000

c 3000

d Increased population will lead to more schools, possibly a nursery, more doctors, possibly a hospital, more services for the elderly, etc.

p.23 Activity Conversion graphs

1

i 19.8 pounds

ii 6.4 kg

iii 19 – 5.5 pounds = 13.5 pounds = 6.1 kg

2

Fruit Cake

170g butter
170g sugar
4 eggs
225g plain flour
pinch salt
225g sultanas
170g currants
55g cherries

p.28 Activity Mean, mode and range

1 1 brother or sister

2 1 brother or sister

3 25 children in class 4

4 30 children in class 5

5 Mean: 32 (brothers or sisters) ÷ 25 (children) = 1.28
This means they have an average of 1.28 brothers or sisters. This is not possible really but we get answers like this for the mean.

6 Mean: 33 ÷ 30 = 1.1. This shows that children in class 4 have slightly more brothers or sisters on average than the children in class 5.

Form for you to fill in

You can photocopy this form and use it to practise the skills you will learn in Unit 3.

Application form

---

application FORM

Briercliffe House

Briercliffe House
Nursing Home
4 Holme Crescent
Briercliffe
Borwick BB11 8SQ

Tel 01287 63407

Please complete this form in black ink or type.

Name ....

Address..

....

....

Telephone Number..

Date of Birth ....

Schools/colleges attended with dates

....

....

....

Examinations gained, please give dates and grades

....

....

....

....

....

Previous employers, dates of employment and job titles

....

....

....

....

Hobbies and Interests

....

....

....

Referees.
Please give names and addresses of two referees

Name ....

Address..

....

Name ....

Address..

....

Foundation GNVQ Health & Social Care © Hadfield, Towers and Wray, 1996.
Published by Thomas Nelson & Sons Ltd.

Unit 1
Understanding health and well-being

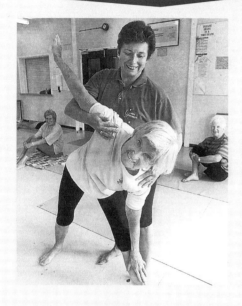

In this unit you will look at the factors which contribute to your health and well-being. You will learn about how your lifestyle could put your health at risk, and how to reduce these risks. You will think about the effect major changes in people's circumstances can have on their health and well-being. You will also look at how people cope with these changes. It will help you to understand:

- how to improve health and well-being
- risks to health.

Plan how to improve health and well-being

This element will help you to understand what factors contribute to your health and well-being and the health and well-being of the people you may work with. By the end of this element you should be able to:

- describe the main factors which contribute to good health and well-being
- identify reasons for improving health and well-being for an individual
- suggest ways to improve health and well-being for an individual
- prepare a plan for improving health and well-being for an individual
- present the plan clearly.

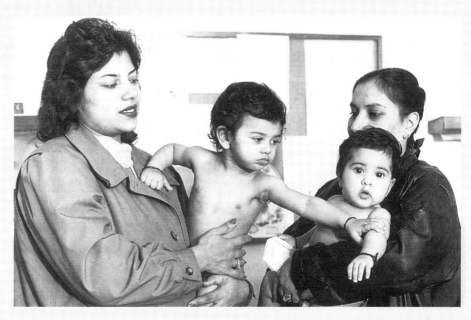

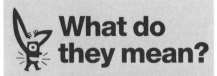

What do they mean?

- **Well-being = feeling good because you are physically, intellectually, emotionally and socially well.**
- **Mobility = being able to move easily**
- **Self-esteem = how people value themselves.**

Health means more than 'being free from disease' or 'not ill'. It also includes your **well-being**.

Activity
What is health?

Make a spidergram like this with **'health'** written in the middle of a page and around it write all the things which mean health to you.

For suggestions on what health is, see page 63.

Why do we need to improve health and well-being?

- increased mobility
- increased self-esteem
- reduced risks to health and well-being.

What makes us healthy?

Three main factors contribute to good health and well-being:

- diet
- exercise
- recreational activities.

Diet

This does not mean 'going on a diet' to lose weight. It means eating food and drink from the seven groups listed below in the correct amounts for your age and **lifestyle**.

There are seven components that make up the nutritional content of a healthy balanced diet:

- protein
- carbohydrates
- fat and oil
- fibre
- water
- vitamins
- minerals.

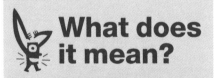

What does it mean?

- **Lifestyle = the type of life a person leads.**

Protein

Protein is needed for the growth, repair and replacement of body cells. Some foods which are high in protein are milk, cheese, meat, eggs, milk, beans and **pulses**. Pulses are an important source of protein for vegetarians.

Carbohydrates

Carbohydrates are found in both starchy and sugary foods. They provide you with the energy you need just to keep your body alive. You need extra energy when you are active. How much extra you need will depend on what you are doing.

Fat and oil

Fat and oil also provide your body with energy. Fat contains twice as much energy as the same weight of carbohydrate. Vitamins A and D are found in fat. Fat in your diet comes from meat, dairy products, fish and nuts, for example. Fruits and other plant sources contain oils which are similar to fat but are liquid at room temperature. You may add fat to your food when you cook it. For example you might fry food in butter, lard, ghee or cooking oil.

Fibre

Fibre is the part of fruit, vegetables and cereals which you cannot **digest**. It is sometimes called roughage. You need it to help your bowels work properly and to stop you getting **constipated**.

What does it mean?

- **Pulses** = a vegetable group which includes peas, beans and lentils.

What do they mean?

- **Digest** = break food down chemically into small molecules which can be absorbed into the blood and used by the body.

- **Constipated** = having difficulty passing faeces (stools), which have hardened in the rectum (back passage).

Each of these has some vitamins or minerals in it and some have both.

 **Activity**
Added vitamins and minerals

Look at some of the food packaging in your own home. Make a list of those foods which say they have 'added vitamins and minerals'.

Activity
Dietary guidelines

Collect advice leaflets on diet from supermarkets, doctor's surgeries and Health Promotion departments ready for the assignment at the end of this element.

Water

Your body is made up of about 80% water. Water is in *all* the cells of the body and in all body fluids such as blood. You could not live without water and you get it from food as well as drink.

Vitamins and minerals

Vitamins help to protect you from infection, and so help to keep you healthy. Minerals play a part in some body functions. They also make up some parts of your body, such as teeth and bones (which contain the mineral calcium) and red blood cells (which contain the mineral iron). Vitamins and minerals are found in small quantities in most of the foods you eat and drink.

Good sources of some minerals and vitamins in a mixed diet

Calcium (mineral)	milk, yogurt, cheese, eggs, sardines, white flour, watercress, cabbage
Iron (mineral)	red meat (especially liver), egg yolk, watercress, cocoa, apricots, brown and white bread
Vitamin B$_{12}$ (riboflavin)	milk and milk products, eggs, meat, cornflakes, yeast spread
Vitamin C	oranges, blackcurrants
Vitamin D	milk, margarine, fish, eggs

Many people eat a lot of convenience foods. Vitamins and minerals may have been added to these foods by the manufacturer to make up for those destroyed in preparation.

A balanced diet

In the leaflets you will find advice about healthy eating, some of which will be similar to the *Balance of Good Health* guidelines (described in the *National Food Guide*). The advice given will probably be similar to this:

- enjoy your food
- eat a variety of different foods
- eat the right amount to be a healthy weight
- eat plenty of foods rich in starch and fibre
- don't eat too much fat
- don't eat sugary foods too often
- look after the vitamins and minerals in your food
- if you drink alcohol, keep within sensible limits.

Look at the diagram below. This shows the five food groups given in the *Balance of Good Health guidelines*. If you eat food from the five food groups in the same proportions as shown in the diagram below you will have a **balanced diet**. Eating a balanced diet will improve your health and well-being.

Fruit and vegetables
Choose a wide variety

Bread, potatoes, rice and other cereals
Eat all types and choose high fibre kinds wherever you can

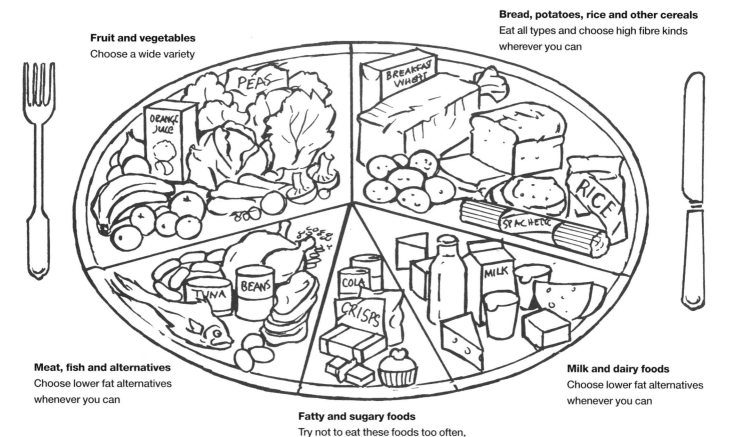

Meat, fish and alternatives
Choose lower fat alternatives whenever you can

Fatty and sugary foods
Try not to eat these foods too often, and when you do have small amounts

Milk and dairy foods
Choose lower fat alternatives whenever you can

The five food groups make up a balanced diet.

 Activity
What I eat

 **For information on health risks, see page 47.**

One simple way to check the overall balance for your diet, is to compare your average daily diet, broken down into the five food groups, with the recommended proportions shown in the diagram. Copy the 'What I eat' chart. Tick the food groups you ate at each meal yesterday. A tick equals one portion. Check how many portions you ate from each group. Compare this with diagram.

What I eat

Meal	Food groups				
	Bread, potatoes, rice and other cereals	Fruit and vegetables	Milk and dairy foods	Meat, fish and alternatives*	Fatty and sugary foods
Breakfast					
Mid morning					
Lunch					
Mid afternoon					
Dinner					
Snack					
Total portions					

* alternatives include poultry, eggs and pulses

 For more on a balanced diet, see page 50.

**Foundation GNVQ Health & Social Care © Hadfield, Towers and Wray, 1996.
Published by Thomas Nelson & Sons Ltd.**

35

Eating the right amount

For your body to work you need to take in energy. In the same way that a car might take in fuel to make it go, your body also needs fuel. This fuel comes from the food you eat. The main energy foods are those containing fat and carbohydrate. Different types of food have different amounts of energy.

If you eat more energy foods than your body needs, any extra is stored as fat and you put on weight. Remember that fatty foods often have a high energy value because they contain twice the energy of carbohydrate for the same weight!

This growth chart for adults shows the usual weight range compared with height. They can use it to find out what is a healthy weight for their height.

Are you the right weight for your height?

The information on this chart is designed for adult men and women only.

Make a straight line up from your weight (without clothes), and a line across from your height (without shoes). Put a mark where the two lines meet. This tells you whether you need to lose or gain weight.

- - - - - - - - - - - - - -

For example, a person who is 5'7" tall and weighs 13 stones is overweight.

☐ UNDERWEIGHT

Maybe you need to eat a bit more. But go for well-balanced nutritious foods and don't just fill up on fatty and sugary foods. If you are very underweight see your doctor about it.

☐ OK

Your weight is in the desirable range for health. You're eating the right quantity of food but you need to be sure that you're getting a healthy balance in your diet.

▨ OVERWEIGHT

Your health could suffer. You should try to lose weight.

▨ FAT

It is really important to lose weight.

▨ VERY FAT

Being this overweight is very serious. You urgently need to lose weight. Talk to your doctor or practice nurse. You may be referred to a dietitian.

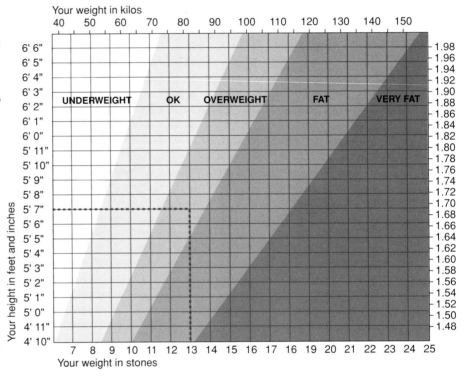

Your weight in kilos

| UNDERWEIGHT | OK | OVERWEIGHT | FAT | VERY FAT |

Your height in feet and inches

Your weight in stones

Exercise

You might be quite happy with the amount of exercise you do. Some people are very active, others are happy to be a '**couch potato**'.

What does it mean?

- **Couch potato =**
  able-bodied person who
  spends most of their time
  just sitting around.

Exercise makes your muscles work. It increases your heart rate (by exercising your heart), which increases the blood flow to your working muscles. The increased blood flow helps your muscles to work better by supplying oxygen and removing waste substances. Exercises that increase the amount of oxygen in the blood are **aerobic** exercises.

Strength, suppleness and stamina

Exercise helps to keep you **mobile**. The reason for this is because exercise can improve the 3 S's:

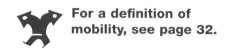

For a definition of mobility, see page 32.

- **strength** – your ability to lift heavy things
- **suppleness** – keeping joints flexible and working well throughout your life
- **stamina** – the way your body copes without becoming breathless or tired.

The table shows the benefits of different types of exercise.

The benefits of some physical activities

● = no real benefit   ●● = some benefit   ●●● = greater benefit   ●●●● = excellent benefit

Sport	Stamina score	Strength score	Suppleness score
Canoeing	●●●	●●●	●●
Cycling (hard)	●●●	●●●	●●
Dancing (disco)	●●●	●	●●●●
Football	●●●	●●●	●●●
Gymnastics	●●	●●●	●●●●
Jogging	●●●●	●●	●●
Judo	●●	●●	●●●●
Swimming (hard)	●●●●	●●●●	●●●●
Tennis	●●	●●●	●●●
Weightlifting	●	●●●●	●

How much exercise?

Activity
How much exercise do you do?

Make a table to show everything you did during one 24-hour period during the last week. Classify what you did as either work, exercise, other recreational activities, eating and sleeping. Remember exercise isn't just about sport. Include for 'other recreational activities' the other things you did apart from exercise, in your free time.

For more on recreation, see page 39.

Time	What I did	Type of activity	Time spent
7 am	Ate breakfast	Eating	1 hr 15 mins
8.15	Walked to college	Exercise	15 mins

Add up how much time you spent exercising during that 24 hours. What percentage of the 24-hour period was it?

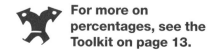

For more on percentages, see the Toolkit on page 13.

Were you surprised at how little exercise you do or were you pleased by how much exercise you do? But how much exercise *should* you do?]

It is recommended that you try to include 20 minutes of an activity which raises your heart rate at least 3 times a week. Of course, these general recommendations may vary depending on your age, health and general level of fitness. You could check what your doctor recommends for you next time you visit the doctors.

Activity
Tracy

'During the week I get up at 8.00. I'm always late up. College is only 15 minutes away, but I don't like to be late so I get my mum to drop me off in the car. Our tutor room's on the third floor so I get in the lift to get there on time. I use the lift at break and lunchtimes too. My mum picks me up at 4 o'clock in case I have to carry my books home. I like to watch the soaps on telly – can't miss any of them. Then I ring my mates and go to bed.

'At the weekend I stay in bed till midday, then go down town and meet my friends at McDonald's. On Saturday night I go dancing at a local youth club but I'm not as good as my mate so I usually stand and watch.

'Sunday I get up late, then I go to my grandma's for a good chat to keep her in touch with what's going on. She's in a wheelchair and doesn't get out much. Then it's back for Sunday tea, watch a video and go to bed early ready for college. Pretty hectic eh!?'

List some of the ways in which Tracy could increase the amount of exercise she does without changing her routine too much.

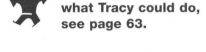 **For suggestions on what Tracy could do, see page 63.**

Benefits of exercise

Exercise helps you become fitter and can help to prevent heart disease. Including exercise in your life and improving your level of fitness is one way to increase your health and well-being. Many people say that exercise gives them a 'feel-good factor'. It gives them a sense of well-being and improves their self-esteem – they feel good and believe they look good.

 For a description of well-being, see page 32.

 For more on self-esteem, see page 90.

Recreational activities

As well as being fun, recreation can benefit you as it can help with your physical, intellectual and social development and well-being.

The benefits of recreation can be divided into these three types:

- **physical development**
- **intellectual development**
- **social development.**

 Can you think of the other benefits you might get, apart from simply enjoying the activities?

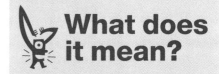
Benefits of recreation

Physical benefits may include improved strength, suppleness and stamina from activities such as sports, dancing, aerobics and walking. This will result in an improved level of fitness.

Intellectual benefits come from 'using your head', for example, reading, watching videos or the television, a new hobby (such as playing in a band), a new course (for example touch typing) or talking with friends perhaps about a film you liked.

Social benefits come from meeting people, making friends (for example at youth clubs), family activities (such as a wedding celebration) and work activities.

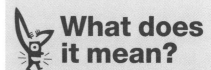
 ## Activity
Recreational activities

Draw a chart like this. Make a list of your recreational activities in the first column. Tick the type of development you think your activities improve. Two examples have been filled in to help you.

Recreational activity	Physical development	Intellectual development	Social development
Swimming club	✔		✔
Reading		✔	

 **Activity**
Something to do

Suggest activities which would help these people increase their self-esteem and improve their physical, intellectual and social well-being.

Taking part in recreational activities will help you to:

● enjoy yourself
● meet people
● relax
● improve your health and well-being
● increase your self-esteem

Doing an activity can increase your self-esteem.

 **Activity**
Recreation and you

1 Record how much time you spent doing recreational activities last week. Fill in on a table the type of recreation and the time spent on them. Now add these up to times to give a total for the week.

Day	Recreational activity	Time spent (to nearest 30 minutes)
Monday		
Tuesday		
Wednesday		
Thursday		
Friday		
Saturday		
Sunday		
	Total	

For help with percentages, see the Toolkit on page 13.

2 Work out the number of hours spent in recreation as a percentage of your total week. Show how you did your calculations. (Number of hours in a week is 24×7.)
3 Work out what fraction of the week this is.

Foundation GNVQ Health & Social Care © Hadfield, Towers and Wray, 1996.
Published by Thomas Nelson & Sons Ltd.

Assignment
Planning to improve health and well-being

Setting the scene
You have been asked by your placement supervisor at the Warrens Information Centre to give a presentation about 'Planning to improve health and well-being'. You need to work through these tasks, and then give the presentation.

Case study
Jason
Jason Jackson is eight years old. He is 1.2 metres (3 feet 10 inches) tall and weighs 27.2 kg (4st 4lbs). He lives in a first-floor flat. He is slightly overweight and his mother sometimes has to get a larger size in clothes than usual for children of his age. His favourite breakfast cereals are sugar-covered. His favourite meal is fish fingers and chips and a popular treat is a visit to a burger bar for a meal with a thick milkshake. He tends to 'snack' throughout the day eating crisps, sweets and biscuits.

Jason doesn't like any vegetables but sometimes eats an orange. His favourite hobby is playing computer games and although he has a bike he hasn't got much confidence and so doesn't ride on it. Because he is a little bit overweight he doesn't like PE at school and is starting to find it hard to be one of the 'gang'.

Task 1
Read the two case studies. Decide whether to base your presentation on Jason, Ellen, or yourself. If you decide to choose yourself you will need to write a short description of yourself and your lifestyle and include information on diet, exercise and recreational activity.

Task 2
List the main features of the individual's lifestyle. Include in this list details of diet, exercise and recreational activities.

Task 3
How could the individual improve their lifestyle to make it healthier? Make a general plan of the main aspects of their lifestyle that they could improve and how they could do it. Include **short-term** and **long-term** goals. Your plan must include suggestions for:
- achieving a balanced diet
- ways of improving levels of fitness
- recreational activities they could take part in.

Your goals should be:
- realistic
- detailed

You could set it out like this:

General plan: Diet

Aspect for improvement	How to improve it	Short-term goal	Long-term goal
eating too much fatty food	grill food, eat fewer chips	start next Monday to reduce fat intake	to become the recommended weight for individual's height

Now do another general guide for fitness, then for recreational activities.

Case study
Ellen
Ellen Brown is 65 years old. She is a retired clerk who lives alone in a small terraced house. She is 5ft 6inches tall and weighs 9st 8lbs. She describes herself as being of average weight but 'going a bit flabby'. She gets out of breath if she tries to run or take part in any exercise. She thinks this is because she has been smoking 20 cigarettes a day, since being 18. She has to take painkillers for arthritis in her hip: two tablets, three times a day.

Her favourite foods are steak and chips, potato pie and spaghetti bolognese. She also eats a yoghurt as a dessert every day. She likes to eat her big meal at night. She doesn't eat breakfast or supper and has a light lunch. She dislikes hot, spicy foods and fast foods like burgers and pizza. She likes to knit, read and watch television. Sometimes she looks after her young grandson. She goes out once a week to meet a friend for an hour, but she doesn't drive and doesn't like to be out late at night.

 For information on health and well-being, see page 32; on diet, see page 32; on strength, suppleness and stamina, see page 37; and on recreation see page 39.

What do they mean?

- **Short-term goal = something to be started or achieved quite quickly, for example, by the end of the following week reduce the number of cigarettes smoked by five.**

- **Long-term goal = something to aim for over a longer period of time, for example, in the following six months cut the number of cigarettes smoked by half.**

Task 4

Prepare a guide for your individual which shows what their new lifestyle would be like for a full week. You could set it out like this:

Day of the week	Diet			Exercise	Time taken	Recreation	Time taken
	Breakfast	Lunch	Dinner				
Monday	cereal, toast, orange juice	salad sandwich (brown bread), fruit, yoghurt	chicken in sauce, vegetables	walk to college walk home aerobics class	10 mins 10 mins 1 hour	phone friends read	30 mins 30 mins
Tuesday							

The likely calorie usage (in Kcal per hour) for males and females is given as follows:

Activity	Male	Female
Sleep	65	50
Lightly active (sitting/reading/writing etc.)	85	70
Moderately active (easy walking/washing/shopping/etc.)	200	160
Very active (hard walking/strenuous physical exercise/etc.)	340	270

Use this information and the time spent on different activities in your table to decide approximately how many kilocalories your individual uses in a day.

What is the average number of kilocalories used per hour? Explain what this means – how active does this seem to make them?

Task 5

Give:

- a report on the main factors which contribute to health and well-being (your work on the activities in this element will help you)
- a list of reasons for making improvements to lifestyle
- the case study of your chosen individual
- the general plans (aspects for improvement, suggestions on how to make those improvements and short- and long-term goals) for diet, exercise and recreational activities
- the guide for your individual which shows what their new lifestyle would be like for a full week.

Task 6

Give an oral presentation 'Planning to improve health and well-being'. Explain your general plan (Task 3) and your one-week guide (Task 4) for this.

You can present your plan in many different ways. You should try to:

- word process your information
- include facts from books and leaflets as well as your own ideas
- include a poster, diagrams and leaflets
- include information, data and statistics to support your ideas. These could be shown on bar charts or pictograms produced on a computer.

You should include a list of the sources of your information. These may be people (for example, Mrs Smith – College Nurse), books or CD-ROM (give name and author).

 For more information on making a presentation, see the Toolkit on page 7. For information on using images, see the Toolkit on page 12.

Opportunities to collect evidence

In this assignment you should cover:

Element 1.1
PCs 1, 2, 3, 4, 5

Application of Number
Element 1.1, 1.2, 1.3

Communication
Element 1.1, 1.2, 1.3

Information Technology
Element 1.1, 1.2, 1.3

?Quiz

How much do you know about planning to improve health and well-being?

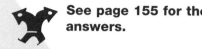 **See page 155 for the answers.**

Before you try the quiz itself, try to find the words which are given at the bottom of the word search. Watch out! The words might go back-to-front and diagonally.

```
C B S E L F - E S T E E M X T
B A M N A E U V P D L X P U S
Y X R Q L S R H T L A E H W A
C U L B T V A P U V R Y D V
D B O X O M X Y S M C C S L I
P M Y W D H S T B A S I I M T
N I J E R P U J E Y N S C N A
M N I N E S Q D P A S E A D M
U E V E B V R I R L D Q L P I
A R E R A M U G Z A D N M R N
W A T G D B T E W F T R O P S
S L S Y S X A S E I P E T V T
V S N Z U A X T U V S R N E P
Q O M L L Z F I B R E P A X I
D S T B T D B O M X W C S J E
M P R O T E I N M Y V F D R L
```

Words to look for

health	protein	digestion
fibre	minerals	energy
sport	physical	exercise

Each question shows more than one possible answer, **a**, **b**, **c** and **d**; only one is correct.

1 What is protein used for in your body?

  a as a main source of energy

  b for growth and repair

  c as roughage (fibre)

  d to fill you up

2 The *Balance of Good Health* guidelines recommend that people:

  a cut down on sugar in their diet

  b keep eating the same amount of sugar in their diet

  c increase the amount of sugar in their diet

  d eat a lot of sweet foods

3 Self-esteem is about:

  a thinking about yourself all the time

  b thinking about others all the time

  c putting yourself first

  d the way in which people value themselves

4 If you exercise and eat a well-balanced diet you are likely to:

  a gain weight

  b lose weight

  c get ill

  d maintain a suitable body weight

5 A vitamin is:

  a something mainly found in sweets

  b something you take as tablets

  c something found in small quantities in many foods

  d something you add when cooking

6 Intellectual activities are about:

  a increasing knowledge

  b meeting people

  c keeping fit

  d increasing stamina

7 You can cut down fat in your diet by:

  a frying your food

  b adding butter or cream to food

  c grilling your food

  d eating a lot of dairy products

8 Which of these foods are not salty?

  a crisps and snacks

  b convenience foods

  c potatoes

  d ham

Scoring

If you got:

● 1 or 2 – you need to know more about improving your health and well-being. You should re-read this section.

● between 3 and 5 – you have a reasonable understanding, but have made some mistakes.

● 6 and above – you have a good understanding of health and well-being.

Investigate risks to health

In this element you are going to investigate the risks to health which are the same for everyone.

By the end of this element you should be able to:

● describe the basic health needs common to all individuals

● identify and give examples of the basic health needs of the main client groups

● identify the main risks to the health and well-being of the main client groups, for different social settings

● describe how best to reduce the main risks to health and well-being and give examples

● describe the effects of major changes in circumstances on health and well-being

● describe ways of coping with major changes in circumstances.

Basic health needs

Basic health needs are the same for everybody:

● **physical needs** are needs linked with the way your body works, for example food and warmth,

● **intellectual needs** are needs linked with the way you learn and the way your thinking develops, for example mental stimulation activities. These activities involve thinking and problem solving like quizzes, tests and puzzles.

● **emotional needs** are needs linked with your feelings, for example the need to feel wanted and valued.

● **social needs** are needs linked with the way you meet people, make friends and form relationships, for example companionship.

For more on health and well-being, see page 32.

To remember these needs use **PIES**:
● Physical
● Intellectual
● Emotional
● Social

Meeting basic health needs

Life stage	Type of need	Meeting these needs
Infant 0–2	Physical Social Emotional Intellectual	Food, warmth, water from parents. Medical support/vaccination for long-term protection from ill health. Carers and family provide social contact. Comfort and pleasure from carers and family. Learning language from family contact and skills from play.
Child 2–10	Physical Social Emotional Intellectual	Food and warmth and protection are provided by carers. Walking opens their world. Developing circle of friends. Greater range of social contacts by nursery, playgroup and school. Very reliant on primary carers for emotional support and to develop their values. Learning through play. Formal education.
Adolescent 11–18	Physical Social Emotional Intellectual	Rapid growth at puberty linked to taking more personal control of supplying physical needs, e.g. food, water, suitable clothing. Peer group (people of same age and interests) becomes very important. Friends become more and more important. A time of mixed emotions needing careful support. Starts to move away from parents to peers for support with emotional problems. Formal education. More learning from experience as new situations are met in life.
Adult 18–65	Physical Social Emotional Intellectual	Becoming self-reliant and a provider of physical support for others (becoming a parent). Develops through a variety of stages including marriage, starting a family and children leaving home. Developing strong attachments to a partner. Might face changes, e.g. divorce, redundancy. Formal education reduces. Challenges come from work roles.
Older adult 65+	Physical Social Emotional Intellectual	Senses become less efficient. General wear and tear means support from others or artificial aids (e.g. spectacles) may be needed. Family will have left home. One partner may die before the other. Movement difficulties increase social isolation. Organised activities support social well-being. Friends and relatives get older and die. Children become independent, emotional support needs to come from other people. Often a time where reduced ability means self-esteem and self-worth could be at a low ebb. Carers need to promote these. Mental activity often outstrips physical ability leading to some frustration. Activities to increase brain functioning are important, e.g. hobbies, reading.

Activity
Types of need

Look at the list of health needs below. Place each item from this list in the correct column on the table. Some of the items on the list can be placed in more than one column.

Fresh air, friends, learning new skills, food, going out, reading, to be liked, sleep, family, exercise, mental stimulation, relaxation, to be clean, watching television, youth club, to be respected, to be loved, to feel safe, to drink fluids

Physical	Intellectual	Emotional	Social
fresh air			

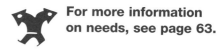

For more information on needs, see page 63.

Check your answers as a group. Did you put some aspects under more than one heading? This is because there are many things that you do which help you fulfil more than one need.

Are any other needs apart from those given in the list shown in these photographs? Add to your list any that you find.

How might a family meal fulfil physical, emotional and social needs?

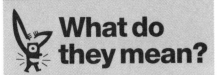

What do they mean?

- **Client** = the person being helped by the carer.

- **Carer** = the helper.

- **Client group** = the people you might help in health and social care, for example children, older people or people with disabilities.

Client groups

These are the main client groups:

- **infants** 1 month to 1 year
- **children** 1–10 years
- **adolescents** 11–18 years
- **adults** (including middle age) 19–60 years
- **elderly people** 60+ years

Basic health needs

Infants

Infants are one of the client groups. They are not able to take care of their own needs – someone has to care for them.

Their needs include:

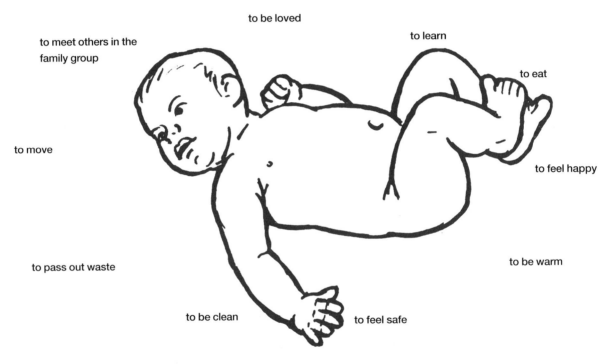

to be loved

to learn

to meet others in the family group

to eat

to move

to feel happy

to pass out waste

to be warm

to be clean

to feel safe

You may have found that basic health needs do not change as people grow older. The *way* those needs are met does often change however.

Activity
Client needs – different or the same?

In a small group, think about the needs of an infant. Look at those shown in the diagram. Can you think of any other needs? Think about the other major client groups. Are their needs the same?

Activity
Meeting needs

Fill in a table like this to show how these four needs are met for each of the major client groups in turn. One answer has been filled in to give you the idea.

	Needs	Met by
Physical	To move about	
Intellectual	To learn	
Emotional	To be loved	
Social	To meet others in the family group	visits to grandparents, aunts, social occasions

Foundation GNVQ Health & Social Care © Hadfield, Towers and Wray, 1996. Published by Thomas Nelson & Sons Ltd.

Main risks to health

Some of the **main risks to health** are:

- alcohol misuse
- smoking
- drug misuse
- poor diet
- poor personal hygiene
- unsafe sexual behaviour
- lack of exercise.

Alcohol misuse

Alcohol is a legal and socially acceptable drug. Many people use alcohol to help them relax and be sociable.

Alcohol affects the brain, causing slower reactions. It therefore affects activities such as driving. It also reduces **inhibitions** which might lead you to do things you would not normally dream of doing, for example, having unprotected sex.

When alcohol is taken regularly in too large a quantity, over a long period of time, **alcoholism** may develop.

The possible long-term effects of heavy drinking include:

- alcoholism
- damage to the liver and stomach.

Activity
Health risks

As a group, **brainstorm** the risks to our health and well-being.

poor diet

too much food

For suggestions see page 63.

What does it mean?

- **Brainstorm** = one person writes down all the ideas called out by members of the group about the topic to be discussed, with no questions asked.

What do they mean?

- **Inhibitions** = the internal controls which stop people doing things they might later regret.

- **Alcoholism** = addiction to alcohol.

so you **think** you can handle **it** ? ...

...**if** you **drink & drive**

DRINKING AND DRIVING WRECKS LIVES

NO EXCUSES

Produced by the Department of Transport to complement the BBC 999 Drink Drive Special

BBC 999

Reducing the risks

You can **reduce the risks of alcohol** by following government guidelines on safe limits.

Safe limits

The Department of Health produces information on the recommended daily limits for alcohol. In December 1995 the government revised the recommended limits to these:

- men should not drink more than 4 units a day (28 a week)
- women should not drink more than 3 units a day (21 a week)
- do not drive for 48 hours after an episode of heavy drinking
- drinking 1 to 2 units a day can reduce heart disease for men over 40 and **post-menopausal women**.

1 unit of alcohol is equal to …

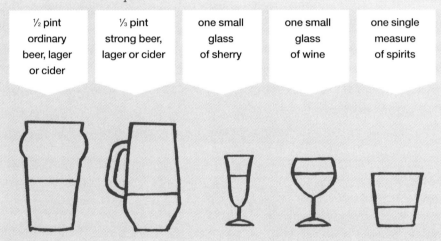

| ½ pint ordinary beer, lager or cider | ⅓ pint strong beer, lager or cider | one small glass of sherry | one small glass of wine | one single measure of spirits |

Smoking

The risks from smoking are caused by:

- chemicals in cigarettes which cause cancers of the lung, mouth and windpipe
- tar and other chemicals in cigarettes which lead to **bronchitis**, **emphysema**, chest and throat infections
- nicotine – the drug in tobacco which causes **addiction**.
- an increased risk of heart disease
- a greater risk of having a low birth weight or premature baby.

When people smoke they also put others at risk, because people around them breathe in their smoke. This is called 'passive smoking' and increases the risk of disease in non-smokers. The risk for young children from passive smoking is particularly high.

Many people who don't smoke find the smell of smoke on people's clothes and breath very offensive, just try smelling a cold ashtray!

Reducing the risk

To reduce the risks of smoking, smokers need to stop smoking completely. Because smoking is an addiction, it is very hard to stop without help. There are products available from your doctor and chemist to help and you may have a local 'smoke stop' clinic.

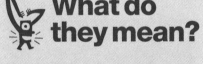

What does it mean?

- **Post-menopausal women = women whose periods have stopped.**

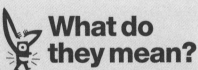

What do they mean?

- **Emphysema = permanent lung damage, which causes shortness of breath.**

- **Bronchitis = Inflammation of the bronchi (the air tubes to the lungs).**

- **Addiction = a habit, feeling that you can't live without something.**

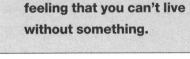

For useful addresses, see page 154.

You can reduce the risk of passive smoking by:

- avoiding places that are smoky
- choosing non-smoking cafes and cinemas.

Many businesses and public buildings are now 'smoke-free'.

Drug misuse

Cigarettes and alcohol are often called **legal drugs**. There are other drugs that are legal to use but are sometimes used wrongly. These are medicines, some of which you can buy directly from the chemist, some of which you get through your doctor. Some people take more than the recommended dose of legal drugs. This is called drug misuse. It can lead to damage to the body.

Drug abuse

Drug abuse is often taken to mean the use of illegal drugs. Some of these drugs and their effects are shown in the table.

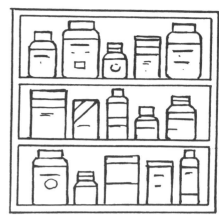

Medicines can be dangerous.

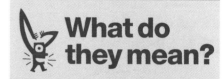

What do they mean?

- Drug = powerful substance able to change body function or behaviour, feelings and how a person thinks.
- Legal drugs = drugs which are either prescribed by your doctor or can be bought over the counter.

Some illegal drugs and their effects

Drug	Use	Effects	Dangers	Street names
cannabis	smoked with tobacco or baked in biscuits	mildly hallucinogenic, increased talkativeness, relaxing	may cause mental dependency, risks associated with tobacco smoking	Resin: blow, dope, hash, hashish, draw Leaf: bush, ganga, grass, homegrown, marijuana, weed, skunk
amphetamines	sniffed, swallowed or injected*	increased heart rate, reduced appetite, reduced tiredness, feeling of alertness	mental and physical addiction, low resistance to disease, heart failure	amphet, billy, speed, sulph, whizz
D-lysergic acid diethylamide (LSD)	swallowed or dissolved on the tongue as tablets or pieces of paper	powerful hallucinatory drug, can produce terrifying as well as pleasant visions	psychological damage, increased risk of accidents	acid, blotter, drop, Lucy, stars, tab, trip
ecstasy	swallowed as tablets or impregnated on paper	similar to those of amphetamines and LSD combined, increased dehydration	as for LSD and amphetamines, risk of kidney damage	doves, E, love doves, M&Ms, MDMA, Shamrocks, X, XTC
cocaine and crack cocaine	usually inhaled or can be injected*	a painkiller, similar effects to amphetamines	addictive, particularly crack, damage to inside of nose and bone from inhaling cocaine, other effects as amphetamines	coke, snow
heroin	injected* or smoked	alertness followed by sleepiness	addictive, high doses can lead to coma	smack, H, junk

* Any drugs that are injected carry an increased risk of HIV and hepatitis infection if needles are shared with others.

The abuse of drugs can lead to:

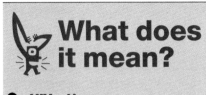

What does it mean?

● HIV = Human Immunodeficiency Virus.

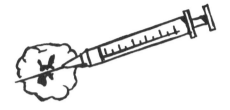

For more on a balanced diet, see page 32.

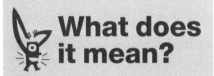

What does it mean?

● Stroke = a blood clot in one of the blood vessels in the brain – resulting in partial paralysis or death.

● increasing drug dependency
● criminal convictions – from carrying or using illegal drugs
● being drawn into other criminal activities and prostitution to pay for drugs
● breakdown of family life as a result of living with someone who abuses drugs
● death – illegal drugs are often mixed with other substances, which could be poisonous. Dealers do this to increase profits
● squalor and poverty
● diseases, such as HIV, from sharing dirty syringes and needles.

Reducing the risk

To reduce the risk of illegal drugs, you need to avoid them completely. When a person who is dependent on drugs tries to give them up, they are likely to suffer from withdrawal symptoms.

Effects of a poor diet

Eating a healthy balanced diet can help to prevent ill health. An unhealthy diet can cause damage to health.

There have been many reports linking unhealthy diet with diseases such as heart disease, **stroke** and some cancers. The government in its *Health of the Nation* paper recommended changes to everyone's lifestyle, including diet, as a way of reducing these diseases.

Eating too little food can lead to ill health, because the body first uses up its stores of fat and then the protein in the muscles, to provide the energy needed to survive. Starvation is very unusual in Britain today.

Effects of too much fat, sugar and salt

Too much fat

You need a certain amount of fat in your diet for your body to work properly. Too much fat in the diet can lead to people becoming overweight, and the build up of a fatty substance in the blood vessels in the body. This causes the blood vessels to narrow (atherosclerosis) and can lead to heart disease.

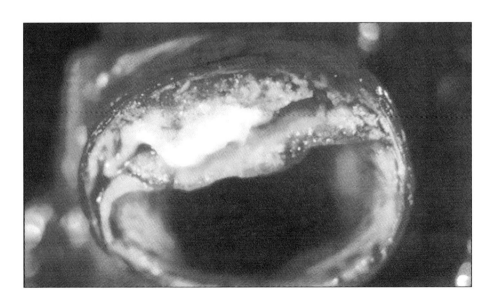

Fat being laid down in the blood vessels of the body causing narrowing of the blood vessel – atherosclerosis.

Too much sugar

Too much sugar can lead you to become overweight. Sugar also causes tooth decay if teeth are not properly brushed. It is not necessary to eat added sugar in your diet. A well balanced diet with enough fruit and vegetables provides all the natural sugar your body needs.

Too much salt

Salt is added to food to give it flavour or to act as a preservative. Too much salt in your diet can lead to raised blood pressure, which can lead to heart disease or a stroke. You do not usually need to add salt to your food as there is enough salt naturally in the things you eat, for example fish and vegetables.

Effects of too little fibre, vitamins and minerals

Too little fibre

Dietary fibre is needed to provide bulk to help food move through the gut (food tube). Too little fibre in the diet is linked to cancer of the bowel (lower intestine). A lack of fibre means that waste moves slowly through the gut and constipation results. Constipation increases the risk of piles and damage to the rectum (back passage).

Too few vitamins and minerals

People only need small amounts of these but if they do not have enough, a **deficiency disease** may result, for example iron-deficient anaemia is caused by shortage of iron. This is common in adolescents who do not have a healthy diet. Lack of calcium in the diet can lead to a weakening of the bones.

If you eat an unhealthy diet you are more at risk of poor health and disease. Being overweight or underweight puts a physical stress on your body which in turn can lead to ill health.

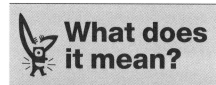

What does it mean?

● **Deficiency disease =** damaging effect on the body from not eating enough of something.

 For more on added vitamins and minerals, see page 34.

 **Activity**
Poor diet

Copy and complete this table.

A poor diet might contain	The effect on the body might be
too much fat	(blocked arteries) atherosclerosis, increased chance of heart attack
too much sugar	weight gain → strain on the heart, skeleton, all body systems
too much salt	
not enough calcium	
not enough iron	
not enough fibre	

Reducing the risk

You can reduce the risks from poor diet by eating a healthy and balanced diet.

Poor personal hygiene

Standards of personal hygiene are usually taught to you when you are a child by your parents or carers. Everyone has their own standards of personal hygiene.

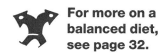 For more on a balanced diet, see page 32.

**Foundation GNVQ Health & Social Care © Hadfield, Towers and Wray, 1996.
Published by Thomas Nelson & Sons Ltd.**

 51

Poor personal hygiene can cause bacteria, virus and fungal infections to be spread between an infected person and others close by. For example:

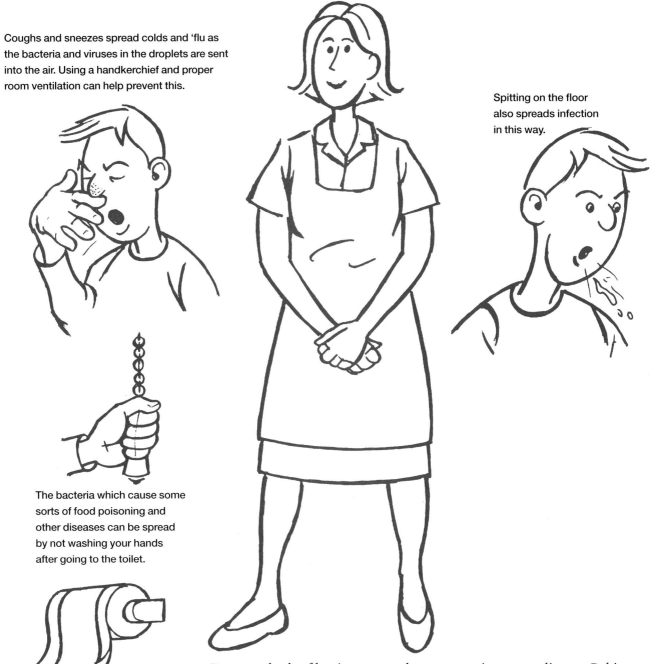

Coughs and sneezes spread colds and 'flu as the bacteria and viruses in the droplets are sent into the air. Using a handkerchief and proper room ventilation can help prevent this.

Spitting on the floor also spreads infection in this way.

The bacteria which cause some sorts of food poisoning and other diseases can be spread by not washing your hands after going to the toilet.

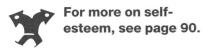

For more on self-esteem, see page 90.

Poor standards of hygiene can reduce your resistance to disease. Babies, young children and the elderly are less resistant to diseases because their defences (immune systems) are not as strong as other people's and so they are more at risk. Standards of hygiene need to be very high where there are elderly people around.

Babies, children and elderly people need more help in maintaining their own personal hygiene. This can include helping them look after their hair, nails and clothing, to avoid health risks. They will also look and feel better, helping to promote their self-esteem.

Reducing the risk

Good personal hygiene is an important way of keeping yourself healthy and preventing the spread of disease. Here are some general guidelines:

wash with hot water and soap to help remove **bacteria** from your body

wash 'sweaty' areas such as armpits, feet and between your legs to help prevent unpleasant body odours (smells)

wash and comb hair regularly to prevent scalp infections and infestation, for example, head lice, and make hair look and feel nice

change underclothes and socks daily to help prevent body odour and the build up of sweat and dead skin on clothing

clean teeth by brushing at least twice a day to prevent the build up of **plaque** which leads to tooth decay and gum disease

What do they mean?

- **Bacteria, virus = small organisms/particles which when taken into the body can produce illness and disease.**

- **Plaque = sticky substance on teeth caused by build up of saliva (spit), mucus (slime), food and bacteria.**

Unsafe sexual behaviour

To be involved in a loving relationship is a basic need. For most people sexual intercourse is part of that loving relationship. There are some types of sexual behaviour which can put your health at risk. Many people have only one sexual partner throughout their lives, others may have more than one. You should know about the risks of unsafe sexual behaviour.

Unsafe sexual behaviour is:

● **unprotected sex**
● sex with a number of partners (especially if unprotected).

Sex is the act that begins a pregnancy. Many people will want to express their love for their partner without the risk of a pregnancy and will use contraceptives to prevent a pregnancy.

Methods of contraception

Sexual activity involves the passing of body fluids between partners. Sperm is passed in a fluid from the male to the female. Vaginal secretions pass from the female to the male. Just like other body fluids, these can pass diseases between partners.

One method of contraception, the condom, is very effective at preventing diseases being transferred between partners.

Sexually-transmitted diseases

These are some of the diseases that can be transmitted sexually:

● gonorrhoea
● syphilis
● HIV (which causes AIDS)
● wart virus (Herpes)
● thrush and other fungal infections
● NSU (non-specific urethritis).

What does it mean?

● **Unprotected sex = 1. not using a condom which gives some protection against infection and prevents an unplanned pregnancy; 2. not using other types of barrier or chemical contraceptive which prevent an unplanned pregnancy.**

Activity
Contraception

● Working in a small group list the methods of contraception that you know.
● When you have made your list, visit your local Pregnancy Advisory Service, Brook Advisory Service or Family Planning clinic where you can collect leaflets. You will find their addresses in a telephone directory. Telephone before you go to find the times they are open. After your visit add to your list any methods you left out.
● Using your information, produce a factsheet about the clinic. You could word process your factsheet.

The results of some sexually transmitted diseases can be ill health. Some of these diseases can even result in **infertility**, cervical cancer or death. It is important to know how to reduce the risks and prevent ill health.

Reducing the risks

You can reduce the risks from unsafe sexual behaviour:

● the condom offers effective protection from the risks but must be put on before starting any sexual activity

● the more sexual partners you have, the greater the risk of contracting a sexually transmitted disease (STD).

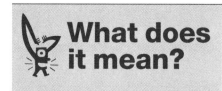

What does it mean?

● Infertility = inability to get pregnant.

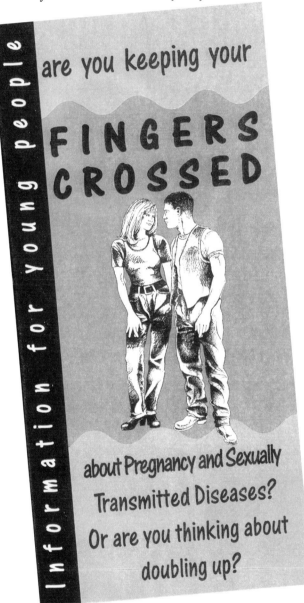

Lack of exercise

Lack of exercise can increase the risk of ill health.

Play is the natural exercise for children, but some children are falling into the habit of just sitting at home, watching television and videos or playing computer games. Parents may not be interested in sport and exercise and may not encourage their children to be interested. Families on a low income may find some sports too expensive, but walking, swimming, running and dancing are excellent cheap forms of exercise.

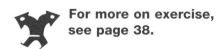

For more on exercise, see page 38.

For older people, who have not been very active, it is important to introduce exercise gradually and build it up slowly. Some types of exercise are particularly suitable for older people. One example is yoga, which can help to maintain the suppleness of the joints. Many sports centres have special sessions for older people so that they do not feel they are in competition with younger people.

Reducing the risks

You can reduce the risks from lack of exercise by drawing up an exercise programme to gently increase the amount of exercise you do.

The risks in public and private settings

Everyone carries on their lives in two main **social settings**: public settings and private settings. For example, the home is a private setting, whilst schools, youth clubs, and leisure centres are public settings.

A private setting

A public setting

Activity
Public and private social settings

leisure centre, home, school, relative's home, college, cinema, boyfriend's home, girlfriend's home, shops, library, countryside, religious centre, skating rink, community centre, nursery, health centre, kitchen at home

Copy the table and place each setting from the list under the heading you think best describes it.

Public setting	Private setting

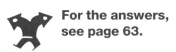

For the answers, see page 63.

Major life changes

You may have heard life described as a journey that starts at birth and ends at death. Sometimes this is called your **lifespan**.

During your lifespan you pass through several life stages which reflect certain changes. These changes are usually linked to physical and emotional development, for example puberty.

Other major changes can happen during your life. These changes are linked with emotional and intellectual development and are often called **milestones**. Marriage is one example of a milestone.

All these changes can affect your health and well-being.

The effects of changes

Some changes in your life will be planned and you will have some control over them, for example, getting married. Some changes may be unplanned and you may have no control over them, for example losing a job.

Some major life changes are:

   loss or bereavement (caused by the death of someone close to you or a pet)

   divorce

   unemployment

   redundancy

   moving house

   changing schools.

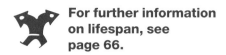

For further information on lifespan, see page 66.

 **Activity**
Life changes

1 Think of some of the things that have happened to you, that have caused major changes in your life – you do not have to include anything you would prefer not to.

2 Make a list of these things/life events.

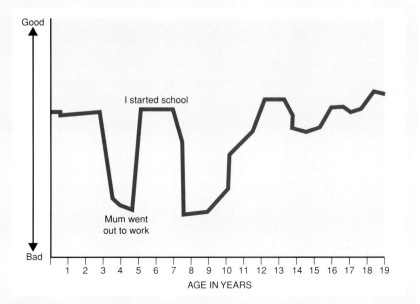

3 You might want to share your list with someone you feel comfortable with and tell each other about the changes. You might feel that to share some of these things would be upsetting, so be sensitive to each other's feelings.

Activity
A number of changes

Look at the case study of Rabena. Are there any similarities with your own life?

Case study

Rabena

Rabena is 16 years old, she recently moved to Burnden from Leighby more than 50 miles away. Rabena has one younger sister and two younger brothers. They moved because her father lost his job as a weaver and found a new job in a mill in Burnden.

Her father tried to travel to work in Burnden so that his family would not have to move from Leighby and disrupt their schooling, but Rabena's mother was finding it difficult to cope without her husband around, because her spoken English was limited. Both sets of grandparents still lived in Pakistan so they were unable to help Rabena's parents with childcare. This meant that the main responsibility for looking after the younger children was falling on Rabena. She missed a lot of school time and then had poor GCSE results. Rabena's father decided to move the family to Burnden so that they could be together, and so that Rabena could finish her education at college.

1   Rabena's life has been affected by a number of changes. Make a list of them.
2   What effects might these changes have on Rabena? For example, think about how looking after her brothers and sisters might affect her.

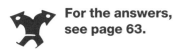

For the answers, see page 63.

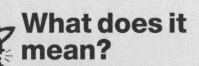

What does it mean?

- **Emotional stability** = when our emotions are balanced and we do not feel too much of any one emotion for too long.

Some changes have a more serious effect on your physical health and well-being than others, but changes usually bring with them some feelings of loss of control, uncertainty about what to do and anxiety for the future. Sometimes major changes can affect your **emotional stability** and social activities. In this case, you may develop low self esteem, high anxiety levels or both.

Activity
The effects of change

This is how change might affect you.

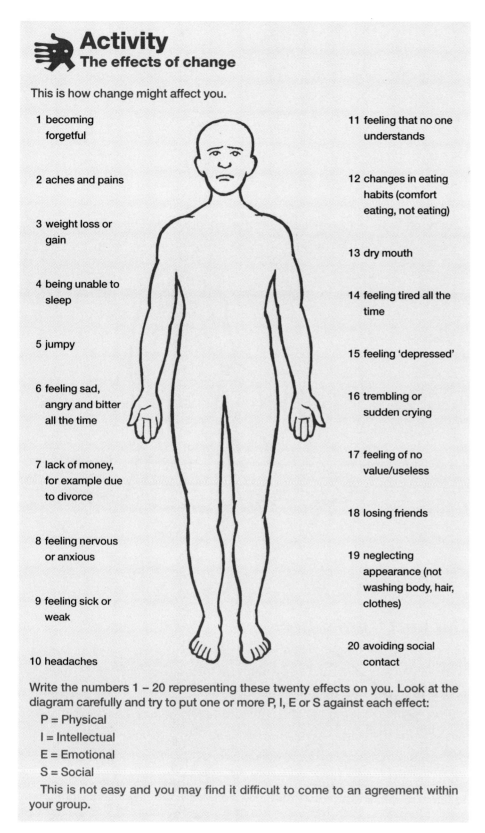

1 becoming forgetful

2 aches and pains

3 weight loss or gain

4 being unable to sleep

5 jumpy

6 feeling sad, angry and bitter all the time

7 lack of money, for example due to divorce

8 feeling nervous or anxious

9 feeling sick or weak

10 headaches

11 feeling that no one understands

12 changes in eating habits (comfort eating, not eating)

13 dry mouth

14 feeling tired all the time

15 feeling 'depressed'

16 trembling or sudden crying

17 feeling of no value/useless

18 losing friends

19 neglecting appearance (not washing body, hair, clothes)

20 avoiding social contact

Write the numbers 1 – 20 representing these twenty effects on you. Look at the diagram carefully and try to put one or more P, I, E or S against each effect:

P = Physical

I = Intellectual

E = Emotional

S = Social

This is not easy and you may find it difficult to come to an agreement within your group.

For more on PIES, see page 44.

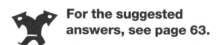

For the suggested answers, see page 63.

Coping with change

Much of the anxiety or stress caused by change is due to the fear of what might be around the corner, the sensation of not being in control, or feeling insecure.

If you are to prevent the long term effects of stress then learning to cope with change is vital. You can learn to improve the way you cope with change to help to reduce the effects of stress.

Finding time to relax

It is important for your health and well-being to find time to relax. Doing an enjoyable activity and finding time to relax can also help to reduce stress. Too much stress can be harmful to health, and can lead to high blood pressure and heart disease. Too much stress can also make you feel irritable and depressed.

Many people find it helps to read a book, listen to music or have a hot bath. Breathing exercises, yoga, massage, meditation and aromatherapy are some examples of other aids to **relaxation**.

Some changes in life such as marriage, childbirth and birthdays are happy events, but even happy events can cause stress!

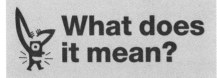

What does it mean?

● **Relaxation = releasing the tension in your body.**

Support from others

You may have found that when you needed help to cope with change, you were able to get emotional **support** from friends and/or family. Some people find religion a helpful source of support.

Some people have no-one they can turn to for support, and instead use services provided either by the government or by a charity. There are professional support services for people with many types of problem. For example, Alcoholics Anonymous (AA) can help with alcohol problems, and Relate or the Brook Advisory Clinic can help with relationship problems. Citizens Advice Bureau can help with legal problems, benefits and many other things.

What does it mean?

● **Support = help, a listening ear, just 'being there'.**

Activity
Support services

Find out where your nearest support services are for people with alcohol problems, and for people with relationship problems. You could use the *Yellow Pages* or contact the Citizens Advice Bureau.

 For help with your research, see the Toolkit on page 3.

Personal care

Paying attention to **personal care**, (diet, hygiene, recreation and exercise), can also help you cope with change. This is because you will maintain your health and well-being by looking after yourself properly. The whole of this Unit has helped you to understand the benefits of good health and how to improve or maintain it.

Assignment
The Park View Centre

Setting the scene
You have been asked to produce a booklet for Park View Centre. The booklet will be given to college students attending the centre for work experience to help them understand the health needs of their clients.

Task 1

Choose a photograph or illustration from a magazine or draw a client from one of the main client groups. Underneath it say which of the main client groups this person belongs to and describe the needs they share with other client groups.

Task 2

Take a separate page for each of these client groups: infants, children, adolescents, adults, elderly people.

For each page, choose an illustration to show that client group. List their basic health needs. For each client group pick a different *basic* health need and describe it in more detail. Include a description of how these needs are met. When you have completed all your pages, design and print out a front cover using a computer and staple the pages together into a booklet.

For more on the basic health needs, see page 44.

Task 3

Your supervisor at Park View Centre has asked you to take part in a survey of the clients who attend the centre to find out about risks to their health. You decide to interview some of the youth group, aged 14–16, and some of the luncheon group, aged 65+.

For your two client groups design a survey which asks members what they think are the main risks to their health:

● in a public setting such as a day centre
● in a private setting such as at home.

Use the eight main risks to health as your headings and ask those you interview to select the four main risks.

For advice on how to produce a survey, see the Toolkit on page 4.

Plan to survey at least 10 people in each of your two chosen groups. From your completed surveys pick out the four most common risks identified by people in the public setting and private setting.

Word process your report to the Parkview Centre supervisor. Your report should look at the main risks to health, listing the four highest risk areas identified in your survey suggesting how to reduce them.

Task 4

The supervisor at Park View Centre is setting up a support group for people who may be under stress. She has asked you to produce a leaflet which will give information to members of staff about the effects of change and how to cope.

For major life changes, see page 57.

For your leaflet you will need to choose three major life changes. Choose from the list of major changes provided on page 57. For each life change describe the effect it could have on an individual's physical health, social activities and emotional stability. In each case describe how people can cope with these life changes. You should include:

● support from family and friends
● support from professionals.

Word process your leaflet. Include illustrations and addresses if you think they would be helpful.

You might like to share the activity in your group and each take one major life change and research the detail about help and support. You could put this work together to make one leaflet.

For more on writing skills, see the Toolkit on page 10.

Opportunities to collect evidence

In this assignment you should cover:

Element 1.2
PCs 1, 2, 3, 4, 5, 6

Communication
Element 1.1, 1,2, 1.3

Information Technology
Element 1.1, 1.2, 1.3

?Quiz

How much do you know about investigating risks to health?

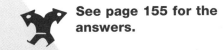

See page 155 for the answers.

Can you find the hidden words?

```
B R C I D O X A S T O L G S O
I A B C D D E S N D Y P H T P
S H U P J O V I T N P R K L T
N F G R I C N Y R S O L R B I
T E S A L T D R U G S N J L C
W X E T I O X O F U Q E U N R
Z E T N S R H Y G I E N E T A
I R T I D C D A B N T P R G P
N C E Y N F R A Y A E N T E S
P I R X H J L M E E J R E N U
T S A L C O H O L R N P B S E
B E G L Y M N S Y J N Y R I S
S Z I E M R L O B N E N P I F
R P C Y H L O M W S W D N Z V
```

Words to look for

hygiene	sugar	fats	alcohol
cigarettes	drugs	fitness	sleep
doctor	fibre	salt	exercise

Each question shows more than one possible answer, **a**, **b, c** and **d**; only one is correct.

1 Basic health needs are *best* described as needs which:

   a apply only to children

   b are important in the elderly

   c are common to all client groups

   d are physical needs such as exercise

2 Which of the following was not listed as a *basic* health need?

   a physical needs

   b intellectual needs

   c cultural needs

   d emotional needs

3 Social health is about:

   a meeting people and making relationships

   b learning about one's body

   c getting money for being out of work

   d eating a variety of foods

4 Which of the following gives the greatest risk to health?

   a being happy in your job

   b reducing daily tobacco intake from 10 to 8 cigarettes

   c becoming a vegetarian

   d reducing the sugar in your diet

5 What are the sensible recommended drinking levels per week, if a person wants to avoid damaging their health? Is it:

   a women 10 units, men 15 units

   b women 14 units, men 21 units

   c women 21 units, men 28 units

   d women 28 units, men 35 units

6 Which of the following is *not* a public social setting?

   a library

   b home

   c youth centre

   d college

7 Which of the following is *not* a major life change?

   a starting school

   b getting married

   c moving house

   d short-term illness

8 One of the effects of stress is

   a feeling happy

   b feeling tired

   c feeling relaxed

   d feeling increased self-esteem

9 Which of the following would be the *best* action to take when helping someone who is suffering from stress?

   a avoid the subject, as it may embarrass them

   b be available to listen and support them

   c just ignore them

   d tell them to pull themselves together

Scoring

If you got:

● 1 or 2 – you need to know more about reducing the risks to health.

● between 3 and 5 – you have a reasonable understanding but made some mistakes.

● 6 and above – you have a good understanding of reducing the risks to health.

Answers

p.32 **Activity What is health?**

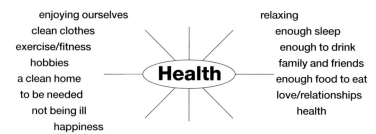

enjoying ourselves
clean clothes
exercise/fitness
hobbies
a clean home
to be needed
not being ill
happiness

Health

relaxing
enough sleep
enough to drink
family and friends
enough food to eat
love/relationships
health

p.38 **Activity Tracy**

find an activity to do around home

walk to the video hire shop

go to a sports centre to swim or learn another sport

take part in an aerobics or other exercise class

take her grandma out in her wheel chair

walk to and from college

take the stairs instead of the lift

join in with her friend when she's dancing

p.45 **Activity Types of need**

Physical	Intellectual	Emotional	Social
fresh air food sleep exercise to be clean	learning a new skill reading mental stimulation watching television youth club	friends going out to be liked family youth club to be respected to be loved to feel safe	friends going out to be liked family watching television

p.47 **Activity Health risks**

lack of exercise

unsafe sexual behaviour

poor personal hygiene

smoking

type of job you do

pollution

poor diet

weather

too much alcohol

p.56 **Activity Public and private social settings**

Public setting	Private setting
leisure centre school college cinema shops library countryside religious centre skating rink community centre nursery health centre	home relative's home boyfriend's home girlfriend's home kitchen at home

p.58 **Activity Rabena**

Changes in Rabena's life were:

- moving to a different town
- missing school
- looking after younger brothers and a sister
- starting at a new college

Effects of these were:

Moving to a different town –

- loss of friends and social contacts
- having to make new friends
- change of school

Missing school –

- not being able to study her course and complete her work
- poor exam results
- unable to find work
- losing confidence and self-esteem

Looking after younger sister and brothers –

- feeling tired
- feeling irritable with her brothers and sister
- not being able to attend social events to make new friends

Starting at a new college –

- having to make new friends
- having to start a new course

p.59 **Activity The effects of change**

1 I 2 P 3 P 4 P 5 E 6 E 7 S 8 E
9 P 10 P 11 E 12 P 13 P 14 P
15 E 16 P 17 E 18 S 19 P 20 S

Unit 2

Understanding personal development and relationships

In order to care for other people successfully you need to understand people and their relationships with others. Understanding your own development, and your relationships with others will help you do this.

This unit helps you to understand:

- all the life stages, and what development takes place at each stage, as well as those things that can make a difference to the way you develop
- relationships formed at the different stages of life, and how these relationships can also make a difference to your development
- relationships between carers and their clients, and how to overcome some problems.

Investigate personal development

Learning more about personal development will help you understand yourself and other people better. This can help you to form positive and rewarding relationships in your life.

By the end of this element you should be able to:

- identify when the main life stages occur in personal development
- describe the main characteristics of each main life stage of personal development
- describe the social factors which influence personal development
- describe the economic factors which influence personal development
- identify the economic and social factors influencing an individual's personal development.

How do people develop?

Physical development, like growing taller and getting heavier is not the only way in which we develop.

 Can you think of any other ways in which people develop? Are there other ways in which the people in the pictures below will have changed as they became older?

Did you think of:

learning to think and reason; developing knowledge and understanding of things?

– **intellectual development**

learning about feelings; being sad, being happy, and learning about the different ways in which you can respond to those feelings?

– **emotional development**

learning to play and share with others; learning to get on with people?

– **social development**.

One easy way to remember these types of development is to think of the word PIES:

Physical development

Intellectual development

Emotional development

Social development

Life stages

The four types of development continue throughout your life, through all the life stages. As you find out about the life stages remember that these types of development are not separate from each other. One type of development can affect another. For example children who find it difficult to talk clearly (physical development) might have difficulty making friends (social development). An older person whose hearing and eyesight is failing (physical development) might feel isolated and even depressed (emotional development).

Main life stages

Infancy   Infants 1 month to 1 year

Childhood   1 – 10 years

Adolescence   Adolescents 11 – 18 years

Adulthood   Adults (including middle age) 19 – 60 years

Old age   Older people 60+ years

Throughout these main life stages there are important indicators of development which show us whether a person's development is within the normal range for their age. These indicators are called **developmental milestones.** These milestones do not occur at exact ages – they occur within an age range.

Infancy

Babies develop very quickly. Their rate of development depends on several things:

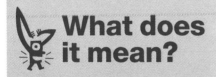

getting the right foods and nutrition

how healthy the baby is

genes passed on from the baby's parents

how much encouragement and stimulation the baby receives

how much love and care the baby receives

Physical development

When they are newborn infants are helpless but gradually gain control over their bodies.

For example:

- At one month they start to hold their head up for a few seconds.
- At 6 months they can keep their heads in an erect position and their backs are straight when they are held in a sitting position.
- At 12 months they can rise to a sitting position from lying down and can sit well on the floor for an indefinite time.

- At one month they can only lie.

- At 6 months they can gradually roll over

- By 12 months they can crawl or bear walk. They can pull themselves to standing, and walk holding on to furniture and stepping sideways.

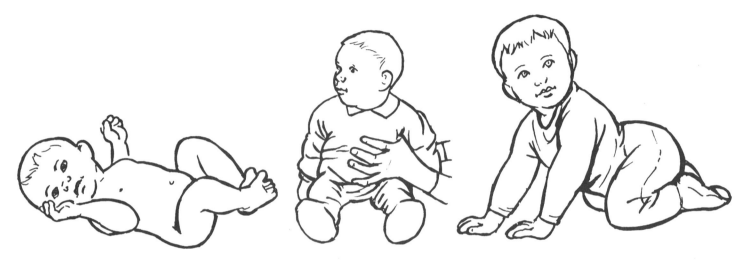

Intellectual development

Both the babies' genes and their **environment** will influence the development of their thinking, their reasoning and their ability to communicate. Some people think that there is no point talking to young babies because they will not understand or answer. In fact talking to them is a very important part of their language development – they will learn about taking turns in conversation, and about listening.

What does it mean?

- Environment = surroundings.

Are there objects to look at and a variety of things going on?

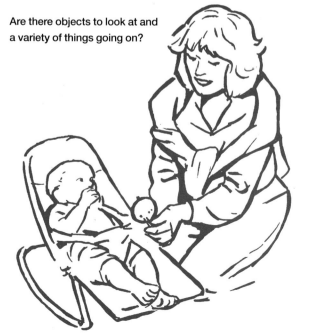

Do parents and others talk to the infant, smile at him, play with them?

- At about 6 weeks infants begin to coo when someone speaks to them.
- By 6 months they make noises in a sing-song way saying things like 'goo, der, aroo, adah'.
- By 9 months they babble loudly in long repetitive strings like 'adad-dad, mam-mam, agaga'.
- By 12 months the sounds they make contain most vowels and many consonants, and sound like conversation. They understand much more than they can say.

Emotional development

Infants' emotional development is influenced by their environment. They make **bonds** with their carers, especially with the one who is the mother figure (primary carer).

Affectionate bonds are formed at various times in your life, but the ones formed in infancy are especially important. Close contact with the **mother figure**, especially touching and holding, gives babies a sense of security. Early security and the development of trust helps people to become stable and secure adults.

Social development

You may not really think that babies have a social life, but from the first few weeks after they are born they begin to **interact** with others. At first this communication is especially with the mother figure.

Even at one month infants will turn to look at a nearby speaker's face, and at 5 to 6 weeks will make some vocal sounds when someone speaks to them.

At about 3 months infants show their enjoyment of bathtime and other caring routines – they often respond with pleasure, and sometimes coo and smile. They like being tickled and talked to.

By 6 months they are still friendly with strangers, but may get anxious when the mother figure is out of sight.

By 9 months infants play peek-a-boo and will imitate hand clapping; they are really becoming very social. They often want to feed themselves and try to grasp the spoon when being fed.

By 12 months old infants can drink from a cup with very little help. When being dressed they hold out an arm for a sleeve and a foot for a shoe. They can play pat-a-cake and wave goodbye.

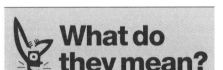

What do they mean?

- **Bonds = affectionate attachments formed with others.**

- **Mother figure = the person who takes the role of mother. This can be a man or woman.**

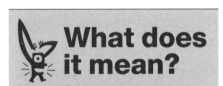

What does it mean?

- **Interact = to communicate with someone who is communicating with you.**

Childhood

1 to 2 year olds

Rapid development occurs from 1 to 2 years and you can see the change from baby to small child. Many toddlers say 'no' to everything and this can be difficult for parents! However, it is just one of the signs that children are developing a separate identity, not that they are being 'naughty'. This sense of separate identity needs to be encouraged, but without forcing children too quickly.

Physical development

Children's growth slows down during their second year, but the body proportions remain similar to the babies', with a large head in relation to the body. Children learn to walk at around 15 months with uneven steps and feet wide apart, and they need to use their arms for balance. By 18 months they do not need to use their arms in this way and by two years old they can walk steadily and run safely, stopping and starting easily. They can push and pull large-wheeled toys and can usually walk backwards to pull the handle.

Intellectual development

By 18 months toddlers learn that certain actions will bring certain results and they will do some things knowing what will happen. For example, they know that a tower of bricks will fall over when pushed. Experimenting in this way increases children's knowledge about the world around them. Play is a very important part of the toddlers' intellectual development and so making provision for play is very important. Toddlers do not need expensive toys – inexpensive ones can be just as good.

Emotional development

Toddlers' emotions can change from moment to moment and they cannot control their changes in mood very well. However, when they do have a temper tantrum their attention can usually be diverted fairly easily to something else. They are learning how to get their needs met: at 2 years old they do not understand that it is not possible, or desirable, to have everything or do everything they want. They are still very dependent, especially upon their mother figure and even at 2 years may be very 'clingy', and constantly demanding attention.

Social development

By 18 months toddlers can feed themselves quite well and by 2 years can usually feed themselves competently on their own. They are usually dry by day but not through the night.

By 18 months they have not yet learned how to play with other children. By 2 years they will play quite contentedly *near* other children, but not yet *with* them. They will defend their own possessions and have no idea of sharing play things or of sharing an adult's attention. Going to playgroup can be an important part of children's social development, helping them learn to share and mix with other children.

Activity
Play

1. With a partner, think of a play activity suitable for a 1 – 2 year old that does not require expensive equipment, and can be done indoors.
2. Check with your tutor that the activity you have thought of is suitable in every way for this age group.
3. Make a plan of things needed and time required to carry out the activity.
4. Arrange with your partner and your tutor to carry out the activity in your next class.
5. When you have carried out the activity write a brief description of what you did. List the things you think 2 year olds could learn from this activity, in other words how would it encourage their development.

2½ to 5 year olds

From 2½ to 5 years, children become more independent in many ways. Often this means a challenging time for parents and other carers, as children only know immature ways of asserting themselves, such as having a tantrum.

The chart shows some of the major developmental milestones between 2½ and 5 years.

Physical, Intellectual, Emotional and Social Development between 2½ and 5 years

2½	Physical development	Intellectual development	Emotional development	Social development
	can walk upstairs confidently runs well can jump with two feet together can climb easy apparatus can kick a large ball 	knows full name uses 200 or more recognisable words is continually asking questions enjoys familiar stories and recognises picture in the book recognises self in photographs holds pencils in preferred hand and imitates horizontal line and circle can build a tower of seven blocks uses I, me and you correctly 	 still very dependent on the adult less easily distracted now when throwing tantrums very active and restless and resists being calmed	still has little understanding of sharing playthings or the adults attention watches with interest as other children play and occasionally joins in for a few minutes still mainly plays alone can eat skillfully from a spoon and sometimes uses a fork usually dry during the day and might be dry at night if lifted 
3	walks upstairs on alternate feet, and downstairs climbs nursery apparatus easily can turn corners and avoid obstacles when running walks forwards, backwards and sideways can stand and walk on tiptoe sits with feet crossed can ride a tricycle cuts with scissors 	can build a tower of nine blocks can thread large beads on string may know names of colours has a large vocabulary which is beginning to be understandable by strangers can give full name and sex and sometimes age carries on simple conversations continues to ask many questions, adding, 'where' questions can count to 10 by rote begins to understand differences between present and past 	 less prone to temper tantrums is affectionate and confiding shows affection for younger siblings begins to understand the need to wait for some things	now understands sharing playthings enjoys floor-play e.g. with bricks, trains, alone or with others joins in active make-believe play with other children makes an effort to keep the surroundings tidy eats with fork and spoon drinks from ordinary cup dry and clean by day, few accidents

	Physical development	Intellectual development	Emotional development	Social development
4	 walks or runs without help up and down stairs, one foot to a step climbs ladders and trees can stand, walk and run on tiptoe expertly rides a tricycle can stand on one foot and can hop on preferred foot sits with knees crossed can throw, catch, bounce and kick a ball and can use a bat	builds tower of 10 or more cubes and bridges draws a man with head, trunk and legs and often arms and fingers speech is now completely understandable and is grammatically correct can give full name, home address and usually age is forever asking questions, why, when, how, and asking what words mean loves to listen to long stories, and tells stories but sometimes confuses fact with fantasy enjoys jokes can count by rote to 20 or more appreciates past, present and future time 	 general behaviour is more independent and self willed is sometimes 'cheeky' to adults prone to quarrelling with playmates when things don't go their way shows sense of humour alternately co-operative and aggressive with adults and playmates shows concern for younger siblings and for playmates in distress	understands taking turns as well as sharing less tidy than at 3 years needs companionship of other children understands the need to argue with words instead of blows eats skillfully with spoon and fork washes and dries hands brushes teeth can dress and undress except for laces and ties and buttons at the back 
5	can walk easily on a narrow line can run lightly on toes likes climbing, sliding, digging and swinging and can do all skillfully can skip on alternate feet moves with the rhythm to music can stand on one foot for a few seconds can hop 2-3 metres forwards can play all sorts of ball games quite well 	 can build 3 steps with blocks can sew real stitches draws recognisable person with head, trunk, legs, arms and features can draw house with door, windows, roof and chimney can count fingers on one hand using index finger on the other can name four or more colours and can match 10 or more speech is fluent, grammatically correct and only sometimes mixes s, f, th, sounds loves to read or be told stories gives full name, age, address and usually birthday	general behaviour is more sensible, controlled and independent shows definite sense of humour tender and protective towards younger children and pets comforts playmates who are in distress 	co-operative with companions most of the time, understanding the need for rules and fair play chooses own friends can appreciate the meaning of clock time in relation to their daily routine uses knife and fork competently washes and dries hands and face undresses and dresses without help understands the need for order and tidiness, but needs a lot of reminding

5 to 10 year olds

Children's life between 5 and 10 revolves around the family, the school and their local community.

Physical development

Children grow taller and slimmer and begin to develop more adult body proportions. Notice in the diagram below that the boys' rate of change is different from the girls'.

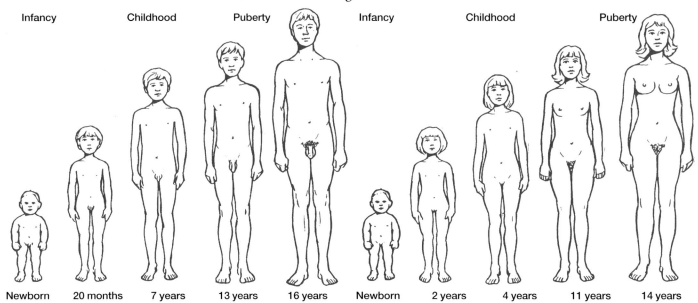

| Infancy | Childhood | Puberty | | Infancy | Childhood | Puberty |

Newborn · 20 months · 7 years · 13 years · 16 years · Newborn · 2 years · 4 years · 11 years · 14 years

Children aged 5 to 10 learn many physical skills. They become more aware of their bodies and want to know how their body functions. Different parts of the body grow at different rates. The brain, spinal cord, eyes and skull are 90% of their adult size by the age of 6. Because motor development is improved, children of this age can take part in more activities than pre school children, for example they can play ball games, climb and run.

Intellectual development

From 5 onwards children's ability to read, write and calculate develops rapidly, and in some societies there is much emphasis on these activities in school. Books are valuable both for children to read on their own and share with others.

Their concentration develops and they are able to spend longer on one task and complete it. Their memory and ability to understand improves greatly. After about seven years, children's logical reasoning starts to develop. As their thinking develops, so docs their sense of right and wrong. They develop **values** and a conscience.

Emotional development

Children of 5 to 10 become less dependent on parents, though it is quite common for them to be upset when they first start school and leave their primary carer, for what appears to them to be a long time. As they grow up, they can usually control their own behaviour better and they develop a sense of pride and self confidence.

This is a stage of making friends. It is mainly through these friendships

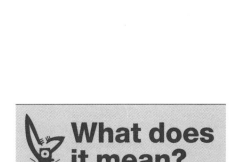

What does it mean?

● **Values = things you think are important.**

that children learn to cope with their feelings. They discover how it feels to be excited, jealous, angry and so on, and how to deal with these feelings. Their ability to cope with their feelings in these relationships will be affected by how feelings are dealt with at home.

Social development

5 to 10 year old children develop relationships mainly with their own age group and often with the same sex. At around 9 years they can start to become very critical of others and sometimes exclude them from their games or from their group of friends.

Children's **self-image** and self-esteem continues to develop.

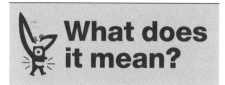

What does it mean?

- **Self-image = how people see themselves.**

For more on self-esteem, see page 90.

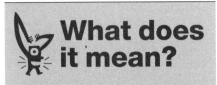

What does it mean?

● **Puberty = when the body changes physically, ready to be able to reproduce.**

Adolescence

Adolescence is the name given to the time from **puberty** to adulthood (ages 11–18).

Physical development

Puberty usually starts earlier in girls at 10 to 13 years of age, and in boys at 12 to 14 years of age.

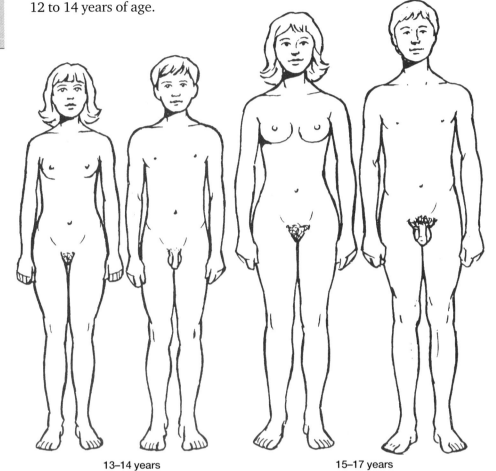

| 10–12 years | 13–14 years | 15–17 years |

Changes at puberty:

Boys	Girls
grow taller	grow taller
pubic hair	pubic hair
penis and scrotum grow	breasts develop
broader shoulders	rounder hips
facial hair	periods start
deeper voice	

Intellectual development

Adolescents' minds can be very creative and they may develop different ideas and thoughts about how to do things or how to behave. Sometimes this can lead to arguments with adults or even with others of their own age. Teenagers need to learn to think for themselves – they will need this ability in the future. It helps their feelings of security knowing that they are able to be independent, to think something out for themselves.

Your experiences, especially in childhood and adolescence can strongly affect the rate of your intellectual development, and whether or not you reach your **potential**.

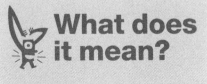

What does it mean?

● **Potential = the maximum an individual is capable of achieving.**

Do you think this boy's intellectual ability is likely to have achieved its full potential?

Adolescence is also a time when your ability to gain knowledge and use it approaches its peak of efficiency.

Emotional development

The changes in hormone levels and the way in which they are released in the body can bring about sudden changes of mood. Teenagers can be irritable, even aggressive, sometimes suddenly weepy and then quite suddenly happy and co-operative again. The feelings can be very strong and a teenager needs help to handle the strength of these feelings and the sudden changes in mood. They need to find ways of coping that are going to be acceptable to others, and which will not lead to more upset and tension for them. Adults need to learn how to handle teenagers' feelings too.

How these changes are handled can affect how teenagers see themselves and how they feel about themselves.

Social development

Many adolescents like to be members of a group and do things together. Their life increasingly revolves around friends of the same or similar age. Sometimes, within the safety of a group and under peer influence, they may try out behaviour that they might not try on their own. This might be risky behaviour like smoking.

 **For more on self-concept see page 90.**

Most teenagers like to spend some time in their own room, even when the rest of the family is at home.

In adolescence relationships with one other person are important. In early adolescence the most important friend relationship may be with someone of the same sex, whereas in later adolescence male/female relationships develop and may become more important. Same-sex friendships in early adolescence tend to be affectionate relationships where hopes, worries and dreams are shared. They are an important, and often fondly remembered, part of your life.

Sometimes individuals are attracted mainly by each other's appearance and body image. This is called **physical attraction**. In other relationships, teenagers may be attracted to another person because of their sense of humour or warm personality, or because they share the same interests.

Towards the end of the adolescent life stage some adolescents choose a long-term partner. In recent years there seems to have been a trend for more people to delay long-term relationships into early adult years.

Late adolescence is the time when most people start a job or begin studying for a career.

Adulthood

Physical development

This is the longest life stage and the one with the least physical development or other developmental changes.

The most significant physical change will be the **menopause**, which happens late in adulthood around the time called mid-life or middle age. At this time the levels of male and female hormones that increased so much in adolescence, and which became more stable in earlier adulthood, begin to reduce. This seems to be more dramatic in women than men, and produces more symptoms. Women's periods become irregular and finally stop at the menopause. They can no longer conceive children once the menopause is complete. The number of sperm a man produces starts to reduce at this stage. However, because there are millions of sperm in any one ejaculation men are usually able to father children until much later in life, as late as 80 years old in some men.

Intellectual development

In adulthood you often need to solve problems, to think things through, and to reason. These mental challenges stimulate your intellectual development.

Your job can demand a lot of thinking and problem solving. Raising a family can pose challenges too. Experiencing success in these areas can help build your confidence.

As children grow older, parents sometimes change careers, or take up new interests. These things can provide mental stimulation.

Emotional and social development

Early in adulthood many people choose a long-term partner, and perhaps marry. These relationships help to satisfy people's emotional needs for love, security and companionship.

Many couples have children of their own, and some who find they cannot have children adopt children into their families. Having children is a very emotional time and brings many changes, especially social ones, into your life. Parents may stay in more than they did before they had children. One of the parents may stop working or change to working part time. Being parents can widen the couple's social circle as they become friends with the parents of other children.

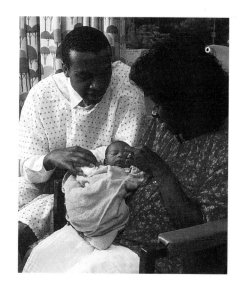

Before you have children it is easy to imagine that it is a totally positive experience, but having mixed feelings once children are born is quite normal.

There are many other things to cope with in adult life. It does not always take a major event to affect your feelings, and sometimes it takes very little. You might just feel low at times and not know why. These feelings are quite normal. Although adults have learned how to be independent, this does not mean that they never need support – they are often glad of it.

Sometimes you might seek support from family or friends, at others you might seek it from outside your present relationships. One of the major aspects of development in adult life is getting to know yourself better and learning to cope with all your feelings.

Old age

'You're as old as you feel.' This saying helps to illustrate how difficult it is to put an age to old age, but the start of the ageing process is usually put at around 60 years of age. The process is very gradual and when ageing starts the rate varies from person to person.

Physical development

There are many physical changes in old age. These are some of the main ones:

- hair loses its colour and usually becomes grey
- hair can fall out resulting in baldness – this is more common in men
- skin becomes drier and loses its elasticity
- eyesight and hearing become worse
- bones become more brittle in old age and break more easily
- joints begin to wear out and can cause pain
- muscles start to shrink – this can lead to reduced height and/or some difficulties in moving about
- changes take place in the brain, which lead to older people taking longer to solve problems and finding it more difficult to remember things
- the ability to absorb nutrients from food deteriorates and this can lead to certain medical conditions, for example anaemia
- infections can cause confusion, which clears up when the infection is treated. This type of confusion can be mistaken for **dementia**
- kidneys become less efficient and do not get rid of waste products as easily
- the pancreas can become less efficient, which may lead to diabetes.

An older person's body is less efficient at maintaining a constant temperature than that of a younger person. In winter this can cause very serious problems because the body temperature may drop very low bringing about a condition called **hypothermia**.

As well as physical changes in old age, there are many things happening at this life stage that affect a person's intellectual, emotional and social development. These include:

- retirement from work
- moving to a smaller house
- friends dying
- grandchildren being born
- living on a pension.

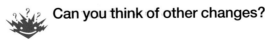 **Can you think of other changes?**

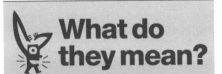 **What do they mean?**

- **Dementia** = a condition that brings about forgetfulness and confusion. It is more common in old age, but is not always part of ageing.

- **Hypothermia** = a condition in which the blood temperature is abnormally low.

 For more on the major life changes, see pages 57 to 59.

Intellectual development

As people move into old age their self image tends to be less positive. This is partly because of the image of old age held in society generally, and partly because of their own ideas. Some physical changes for example hair colour changing to grey might seem minor to others, but can greatly affect your self-image. Other, more major changes, such as retirement, may affect your self-concept.

When people stop work they may suffer **psychologically** because they no longer feel useful. Keeping old interests and developing new ones can help older people maintain a positive self-concept. Being valued for their experience and understanding of life can help too.

You might have discovered from the activity **Newspaper cuttings** that Western society is not very positive about old age. In newspapers and books and on television, older people are often ignored. Sometimes, younger people think of older people as forgetful, stubborn and even somewhat aggressive.

Social and emotional development

Activity
Differences

In a small group make lists to show how each of these events could make differences to the social life of an older person and how an older person might feel.

- retirement from work
- moving to a smaller house
- friends dying
- grandchildren being born
- living on a pension

Event	Social life	Feelings
grandchildren being born	stay in at night to babysit, might meet new people whilst taking grandchild for walk	brings happiness and hope for the future

As people become older they tend to see fewer people and go out less. They may become more contented to centre their lives around the home and a few close relatives and friends. Sometimes people's worlds are reduced more quickly than they would choose, because of disability or the illness of themselves or others.

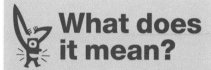

Activity
Newspaper cuttings

Collect ten newspaper cuttings about people aged 60+. How many are positive and how many negative?

For more on self-image and self-concept see page 90.

What does it mean?

- **Psychologically = mentally, in one's mind.**

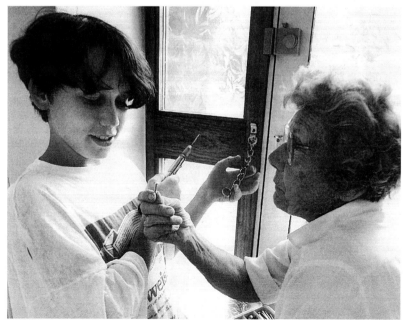

Social and economic factors affecting personal development

Many factors affect your rate of development and most of these can come under the heading of social factors or economic factors.

Social factors

Four main social factors **influence** your development. These are:

- family
- education
- environment
- peer group membership.

Family

What you experience in the family is central to what you learn about yourself and how you view the world around you.

Everyone needs to be loved, to feel wanted and respected and in your early years you look to your parents and very close family to meet these needs. When children are very small they do not really understand what adults call 'good' and 'naughty' behaviour, and they want to be liked no matter how they behave. If children always receive criticism, it is likely that they will grow up with a poor self image.

Other things within your family affect your development, for example how many children there are in your family, whether you are the youngest, middle or oldest child. Children whose grandparents are closely involved in their care will have different experiences than if the those grandparents are more distant or if they have none at all. Some children may have only one parent, whilst others may have step parents. Some families have very close relationships with aunts, uncles and cousins.

Education

The type of school you go to can affect your social development. For example, you might go to a single sex boarding school or a mixed comprehensive. The length of time you spend at school and the different methods of teaching also affect your development.

Peer groups

This is the name given to your group of friends and those of a similar age at school, college or work. The peer groups you belong to will influence how you think and behave. Everyone needs to feel a sense of belonging, and this need can sometimes be so strong that people do whatever others in the group say or do without really thinking.

Peer groups are often an important influence on keeping or changing certain views and opinions. For example, groups of college students often hold the same political opinions. A peer group can lead the way to setting good, or bad, behaviour.

Environment

Your surroundings are the other main influence on your development. If you live in a warm, spacious house that is clean and comfortable you will feel very different about life than if you live in a small, cold and damp house. Housing conditions can also affect your physical health, and if you are unwell for much of the time it can affect the way you feel about yourself. Conditions at home might also affect how well you get on with school or college work. If conditions are unsuitable, for example you have no quiet area to study, you might fall behind in your work, and this can affect the qualifications you achieve.

People who live in a crowded town or city which has a great deal of traffic and pollution may not be as healthy or as relaxed as people who live where there are more green spaces like parks and fields. Easy access to leisure facilities like sports stadiums, cinemas, museums and theatres can make a difference to the quality of your life. Widening your interests and meeting new people can affect your development.

Activity
Jamal's life

1   Read about Jamal in the case study.

2   What kind of a person do you think Jamal is? For example, is he popular, outgoing, shy? Describe the way you imagine him and say why.

3   Make a list of all the social factors that you think have made Jamal into the sort of person that you describe.

Case study
Jamal

Jamal is 15 years old. At school, he likes maths and design technology best and has always been good at those subjects. He is quite sporty too: he is captain of the cross country running team and is in the school football team. He is not good at English or history. He used to enjoy history until he got a new teacher in his second year; he really couldn't seem to get on with her and that changed his ideas about it. Jamal thinks he might like to train for a job in engineering.

Jamal still lives in the town he was born in. His parents had lived in the town for 20 years before he was born. He lives in a terraced house, which is of average size, in the middle of town. It had 3 bedrooms but Jamal's dad is a carpenter and he changed it into a 4-bedroomed house. This means that Jamal and his two sisters, one 13 and one 18, have been able to have a bedroom each. The house is centrally heated and has a bathroom. Jamal has one set of grandparents now; they are his mum's parents, and they live just two streets away. They have lived there for as long as Jamal can remember. Jamal's granny used to look after him after school when he was small, because his mum started a job.

There is a cinema in the town, a library and two night clubs. On the edge of town there is a park and some playing fields. A sports club and leisure centre was built three years ago outside the town. Jamal can get there on the bus or his bike. He spent his pocket money on membership of the sports club and he spends a lot of his weekend and holidays there with friends.

Economic factors

'Money isn't everything'

That is a phrase you often hear and of course it *is* true but how much money you have does influence the kind of life you lead. If you are a child or young person, then how much money your parents have will influence your lifestyle, which can affect your development.

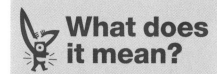

What does it mean?

● Economics = the use of money and other resources.

Activity
Lifestyle changes

1 Read Melanie's case study.

2 How do you think Melanie's lifestyle has changed, since her father's business went bankrupt? Make a spidergram to show the changes.

3 Discuss in small groups how Melanie's development might be affected by economic factors. Make a list of these effects. For example, she might get less chance to play outside with friends now that she is living in a flat instead of in a house. This might affect her physical development and her chances to make friends (social development).

Case study
Melanie

Melanie is 8 years old and she has a brother Jack who is 2 years old. They both live with their parents in a very small rented flat which is on the sixth floor of a block.

Melanie's dad had his own small business that supplied materials for builders, but 18 months ago the business went bankrupt. Melanie didn't really understand but she remembers that a lot of the things they had, including her new bike, had to be taken away. The house they lived in, which had a bedroom each for her and Jack and a small garden, had to be sold. They came to live in the flat. They used to have a holiday once a year and get small presents from Melanie's dad when things were going really well.

About the time they came to live in the flat Melanie's dad started to become ill. Since then he's been in and out of hospital a lot, and she doesn't see him much. This time he's been in hospital for two months. They have enough money to buy basic food each week and pay the gas bill and the rent, but they have none left over. They don't have a telephone in the flat and they have no car. The flat is in the middle of town, whereas their house used to be just outside town. Melanie has had to change schools because she can't get to her old one now. Melanie's mum has thought about getting a job, but the nursery fees for Jack would be too expensive.

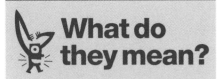

What do they mean?

- **Income** = all money received by a person or family.

- **Financial commitments** = payments that have to be made for goods or services because the person has promised to pay. Sometimes a formal agreement is signed, especially if it is a long-term commitment.

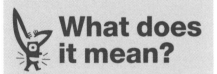

What does it mean?

- **Priorities** = placing things in order of importance.

Income

Your money can come from earnings from your work, or from benefits, which is money provided by the government to help you if you earn little or no money. You might receive benefits if you are unemployed or ill or if you become disabled. You might also have **income** from interest on money you have in a bank, building society or post office. The total income for a family can seem quite high, especially if more than one person is earning a wage.

Financial commitments

You have to make decisions about how to spend your money. You may have some **financial commitments**. These can be long-term like a mortgage or rent, or paying for something like a car over a number of years. They can be short-term, such as putting money into a savings club each week for a few months before going on holiday.

How income is spent

How you decide to spend your income will depend on your **priorities**. For some people it is very important to have a car and they would place this above having other things. For most people in Britain buying a house is their top priority and many people have a mortgage to pay.

It can be difficult to decide how best to spend the amount of money you have each week or month.

Even when things are running smoothly it can be difficult to manage your income so that you do not get into debt. It is even more difficult if your circumstances change suddenly and you find yourself with a smaller income. This could happen by:

- being made redundant
- becoming unemployed
- losing a partner or close family member through death
- having a baby
- getting divorced
- suffering a long illness
- becoming disabled through illness or accident.

Financial problems can make the emotional problems linked with these kind of events worse. These worries and anxieties can mount up and sometimes lead to illnesses such as depression for a few people.

Activity
Making choices

 ## Case study
Jennie and Paul

Jennie and Paul are getting married next April. Jennie is 21 years old and Paul is 24. Jennie left college in July after she had completed an Intermediate GNVQ in Health and Social Care. She worked in a shop when she left school but decided she wanted to do something different, so she went to college for a year. She enjoyed her course and has decided to work in health and social care for one or two years. If she likes the type of work, she would like to go back to college to get some more qualifications to help her to train for a career. She has had a job for three months as a care assistant in a rest home for older people.

Paul started work as a lorry driver for a local building firm, but he did some training to learn to drive the large machinery. He now operates an excavator. He likes the work and has had his current job for three years. The firm seems to be doing well and he hopes to stay there. Paul has a van but it has many miles on the clock and it is costing a lot in repairs.

In their spare time Jennie and Paul are both members of a local brass band in which Jennie plays trumpet and Paul plays trombone. They rehearse once a week and get together with all the other band members every Friday night. Jennie and Paul both like going to the cinema and enjoy holidays. Paul likes going swimming, which Jennie quite enjoys, but she prefers playing tennis.

They both want to live on the edge of town near to the park if they can. The type of house they like costs £35 000 but there are some to rent for £70 per week. This means Jennie would be about two miles from work. The depot where Paul works is about the same distance away, but he often gets sent on jobs several miles away in other towns.

Jennie and Paul's total take-home pay is £320 per week. They have managed to save £3000 which they keep in a building society.

1 Working in groups of 3 or 4, make a list of the things Paul and Jennie might spend their money on, under these headings:

Essentials	Things they would like

2 Discuss the different ways you think they might use their savings. Make a list.

3 Make a list of the kind of things Jennie and Paul will have to find out before they can make sensible decisions about how to use their savings.

4 Share your lists with the whole group.

 **Assignment**

Life span chart

You need to think back through all you have learnt in this element; use all your work and all the extra information and pictures you have collected.

Task 1

Make a chart to include the following:

- name of each main life stage
- age span of each main life stage
- major characteristics of each life stage
- social and economic factors in general which affect your development through the life stages.

You can make the chart in any way you wish, but you might choose to do it like this:

Make your chart large so that you can include all the major characteristics of each life stage. Illustrate your chart with appropriate pictures.

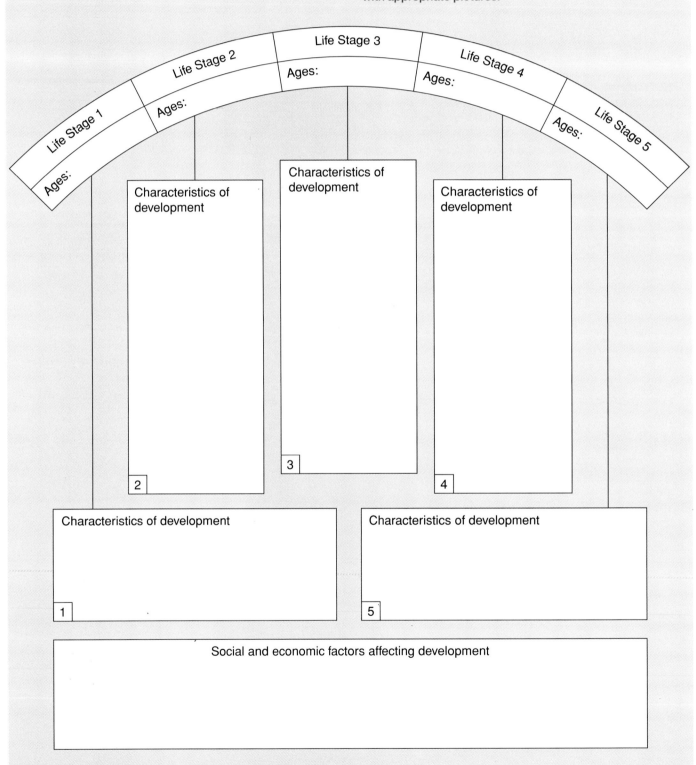

Task 2

Choose one life stage and and describe the characteristics of development in more detail for this one stage.

Put your information into the form of a booklet.

Use pictures to illustrate your descriptions.

Design a front cover for the booklet.

Task 3

Look back to the work you did about Jamal and about Melanie. Include this work with your assignment and make sure you have a clear list of the social and economic factors that affected their life and development.

Task 4

Samina is 21 years old. She has just started a new job. Her pay is £180 per week. One third of this is paid out in tax, National Insurance and pension fund.

● What fraction of her pay does she take home?

● How much money does she take home?

To get to work she buys a weekly saver strip for the bus for £6 per week. She rents a flat for £71 per week and she buys £3 of electricity stamps per week towards her electric bill. These are her 'essential payments'. What is left is her 'flexible money'.

● How much does she pay in essentials?

● How much of her pay is left after she has paid these?

The ratio of her bus fare costs to her electric costs is 6:3 (6 to 3).

This can be simplified by dividing both sides of the ratio by 3, 6:3 becomes 2:1

This means that for every £1 she spends on electricity she spends £2 on bus fares or that she spends twice as much on bus fares as she does on electricity.

● What is Samina's ratio of essentials to flexible money?

● What is this ratio in its simplest form?

● What does this mean?

She decides how to spend her flexible money. She decides to save one quarter and to allow one quarter for clothes. The rest she spends on food and entertainment.

● How much does Samina allow for food and entertainment?

● What percentage of her take home pay does she save?

● Draw a bar chart to show how much of her pay (£180) is spent in each area.

Opportunities to collect evidence

In this assignment you should cover:

Element 2.1
Pcs 1, 2, 3, 4.

Communication
Element 1.2, 1.3, 1.4

Application of Number
Element 1.1, 1.2, 1.3

Information technology
Element 1.3

?*Quiz*

How much do you know about investigating personal development?

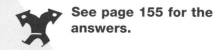

See page 155 for the answers.

Each question shows more than one possible answer, **a**, **b**, **c** and **d**; only one is correct.

1 The development of knowledge, thinking (cognition), language and memory are all forms of:-
  a physical development
  b intellectual development
  c emotional development
  d social development

2 A baby's rate of development directly depends on which one of the following:
  a genes passed on from the baby's parents
  b whether the baby is born in hospital or at home
  c which month of the year the baby is born
  d what type of clothes are chosen for the baby

3 Emotional development is a development of:
  a how a person thinks
  b how a person behaves
  c how a person deals with feelings
  d how a person's body gradually grows.

4 Which of the following is a 3 year old able to do?
  a walk or run alone up and down stairs
  b walk forwards, backwards and sideways
  c stand, walk and run on tiptoe
  d stand on one foot for a few seconds

5 Which of the following is a feature of puberty:
  a loss of elasticity in the skin
  b wounds take longer to heal
  c maturing of reproductive organs
  d cells are not replaced so quickly

6 People's skin normally changes as they age. Which of the following is the most common change?
  a the skin becomes paler
  b the skin becomes less dry
  c the skin becomes less elastic
  d the skin becomes darker

7 Which of the following is a social factor that affects development?
  a intellectual ability
  b income
  c holidays
  d the family

8 Which one of the following would cause a negative economic effect on someone's well-being?
  a a happy marriage
  b being popular at school
  c becoming unemployed
  d getting a better job

Scoring

If you got:

● between 1 and 3 – you are beginning to learn some things about personal development, but still have some gaps in your knowledge. Read the element again, look at your work and talk with friends in the group, and your teacher. Try the quiz again.

● between 4 and 6 – you have quite a good knowledge of personal development. Look up the information for the questions you answered wrongly. Ask your teacher if there are things you do not understand.

● 7 and above – Congratulations. You have done really well. Now you are ready to build on this knowledge with further work on relationships through life.

Explore relationships at different life stages

This element looks at different relationships during your life. You already know something about the development of relationships from your own experience.

By the end of this element you should be able to:

identify relationships formed at different life stages

describe the main characteristics of relationships formed at different life stages

describe the effects of forming positive and negative relationships at each life stage

suggest the effects on your own personal development of these relationships.

Relationships

Different types of relationship are formed at the different **life stages**.

For more information on life stages, see pages 66 to 79.

What different relationships are there?

friendships

working relationships

sexual relationships

parent-child relationships.

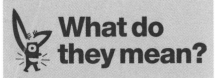

What do they mean?

- **Self-image** = how people see themselves.

- **Self-esteem** = how people value themselves.

- **Self-concept** = the whole idea that you have about yourself.

 For more on positive and negative relationships look at pages 96 to 98.

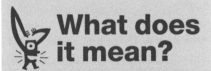

What does it mean?

- **A sense of identity** = a sense of who you are, what sort of a person you are, and where you fit in society.

What you bring to every relationship is yourself. Your self-image and your self-esteem have an important influence on how you make relationships with other people. The two things together, **self-image** and **self-esteem**, make **self-concept**.

Relationships can affect your self-concept, especially your self-esteem. It is easy to have a low opinion of yourself if people around you are always criticising you. When somebody pays you a compliment it can boost your self-esteem. If you are in a relationship with someone who is always caring, this builds up your self-image and self-esteem. When a child grows up in a caring home background, they often grow up to believe in themselves and to be confident.

Relationships can help build your **sense of identity** too. Stable relationships and a certain amount of routine can help people feel secure about their identity. When children have many changes in their lives, their sense of identity will be less certain.

Relationships can also affect the kind of **social activities** you take part in and how much of a social life you have. Mixing with other people in a variety of social activities will help you to be **socially integrated** – you will feel comfortable in a social environment, rather than nervous and out of place. If children mix only with a very small circle of people, perhaps just their close family, they can find it very difficult when they are older to make friends and go to places where they will meet lots of new people. If teenagers are given extremely strict rules about where to go and who to go with, they can find it very difficult to blend in smoothly with society (integrate socially).

How you see yourself and what you think about yourself are just as important as how other people see you and what they think of you.

Activity
The holiday club

You want to join a holiday club you have seen advertised. When you contact the organisers they ask you to provide a short description of yourself.

1 Write the description and include some or all of these points:
- what you look like
- whether you are rather quiet and shy, or more talkative and out-going
- what you like doing
- things you are good at
- things you are not so good at
- a little about your family
- where you live.

Include anything else that you want to say about yourself.

2 Read your finished description through carefully. Use two different colour highlighters. Colour all the things you have said about your self-image in one colour. Colour all the things that you have said about your self-esteem in another colour.

3 Now *either*:
- Share what you have written with someone who knows you in the group. Have you written similar or different things about yourselves? Does the other person see you as you see yourself? Write down anything new you have learned about yourself.

or

- Ask someone who knows you well to describe you and compare this with your own description.

Main characteristics of relationships

The **main characteristics of relationships** are:

- sharing
- mutually supportive
- physical attraction
- assertive
- protective
- dependent.

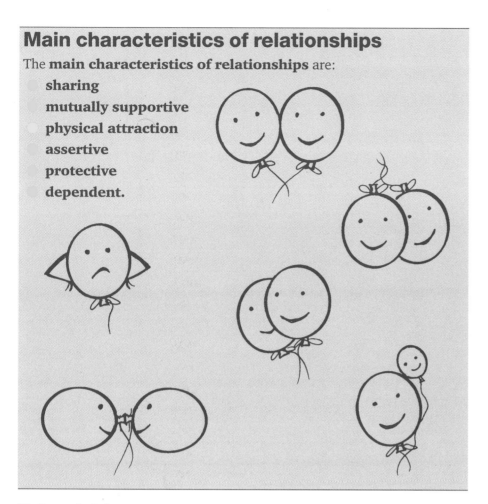

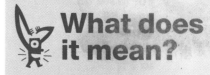

What does it mean?

- **Main characteristics of relationships = those things which are particular to that relationship at that life stage.**

Friendships

 What is a friendship? What is a friend?

The word 'friend' is probably one you use a lot, but what does it really mean?

Are the people in the photograph friends? How can you tell?

For more on bonds, see page 68, for more on social development of children, see pages 68 to 71, 73, 75.

 **Activity**
Friend wanted

1   Imagine you are advertising for a friend.

Write an advertisement for a friend, describing the kind of person you would like your friend to be.

2   Think of someone you consider to be your best friend or someone who has been your best friend in the past. Write a brief description of this best friend. Try to be honest and write about how they really are. You should include some of the things that irritate you as well as some of the things that you like about this person.

3   Look back to the description you wrote of yourself in the activity **The holiday club**.

Draw a table like this, making the columns as long as you like:

Things about me	Same as my friend (tick)	Different from my friend (tick)
I like animals		✓
I like bike rides	✓	

Count the ticks in each column. How many of the things about you and your friend are the same? How many are different? What about the friend you advertised for – did you want him or her to be interested in the same things as you? Is it important for you and your friends to have things in common?

 **Activity**
Friendly discussion

1   Form a small group with two or three other people. Talk about the things you decided you wanted in a friend, and the **qualities** you have found in your friends. Make a list.

2   Discuss the kind of things you talk to friends about. If some of these things are private things such as relationships or health problems, just say, 'private things'.

3   Is it important for you that your friends listen to you? Is it just as important for you to listen to them?

4   Do you, and the others in your group, think that there are different kinds of friendships? How would you describe these?

5   Make a list of all the things that your group thinks are important in friendships.

A friendship is formed when two or more people think a lot of each other. It means people support each other even when things are difficult. It also means a strong bond has built up between people. Even when they disagree it is still possible to keep the bond. Some friendships are lifelong and the bond is never broken. Friendships are usually sharing relationships. This could be a sharing of interests and hobbies. Friends also often share ideas, experiences, feelings and problems. Talking about your feelings and problems with someone can often help you to decide what you want to do.

What does it mean?

● **Qualities** = the good things about a person that make others like and trust that person.

Working relationships

Working relationships are formed at school, college or work. At college you often have to work on assignments or activities with other people. These people can be other students, teachers or tutors.

Many types of relationship are formed at work:

- Some working relationships are **mutually supportive**. This is where people help each other out equally, especially when times are difficult. An example of this could be revising for exams together.

- When a new person starts work someone may choose to look after them, and protect them. This can be very helpful for a time, but if it continues for too long, then the person who was new can become very dependent and never really learn to do things for themselves.

- Some people at work are **assertive** and seem to be able to get what they want, others find this much harder to do. Sometimes two assertive people form a relationship, and both are able to talk about what they want. In other cases, someone less assertive will depend on someone else to speak up for them.

- Sharing is often part of a working relationship. At work a team structure often helps a heavy workload to be shared by members of the team, just as it can at school or college. They also share ideas for solving problems.

- Some people's work relationships develop to become friendships and they meet outside work. Sometimes the relationships continue even after retirement.

Most people start work in late adolescence or early adulthood and form working relationships with others. However, if you think of work not only as paid work, but also the kinds of work you do at school or college, you can think of some kinds of working relationships as forming in childhood or early adolescence.

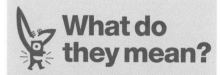

What do they mean?

- Mutually supportive = each one supports the other.

- Assertive = being firm about what you want or need.

What does it mean?

- **Sexual intercourse = the act of having sex; insertion of the male penis into the female vagina.**

Sexual relationships

Some relationships are a combination of friendship and strong physical attraction. This is what is often called a 'romance'. When you are romantically involved with someone, the relationship will usually include some physical expression of your feelings. This does not always mean having **sexual intercourse**; it can mean kissing, hugging and touching. In these relationships people offer emotional support to each other.

After puberty, teenagers begin to feel physically attracted to the opposite sex, or sometimes the same sex. The majority of people have opposite sex relationships, but a small percentage of adults enjoy same sex relationships. Just like opposite sex relationships, same sex relationships do not always include sexual intercourse. The choice to have a same sex relationship should be respected.

People's sexual relationships, including having sex, can continue through middle age and old age. Many people believe or imagine that older people lose interest in closeness and intimacy, but why should this be true? Many people become closer to a partner as they grow older. This closeness can include regular sexual intercourse.

Parent-child relationships

Parents often think of their children as children all through their lives. However, children grow physically, intellectually, emotionally and socially until they can be completely independent of their parents.

Activity
Discussion

Form small groups of three or four. Share your views and opinions about:

- romance
- staying with one sexual partner all through life
- same sex relationships
- sexual relationships in older age.

For more on the main characteristics of relationships, see page 91.

This is quite a slow process and children take time to adjust to increasing independence. Parents take time to get used to the idea that they no longer have to protect the child. Some parents who devote their lives to their children find it hard to cope when their children leave home. Usually, the strong bonds that form between parents and children remain even after the children have left home, and often until the parents or child die. The nature of the relationship between parents and children changes several times over the years, as the children grow and develop.

Activity
Changes

This is a chart of a parent-child relationship at different life stages.

1 Look at the symbols on page 91 which show the characteristics of relationships.

2 Copy the chart below, leaving space to draw the symbols next to each life stage.

3 Draw the symbols which you think show the characteristics for each life stage. Use two different colours to show which is the parent and which is the child. The first box has been done as an example.

Child: birth to 3 yrs Parents 21 yrs to 24 yrs	
Child 4 yrs to 10 yrs Parents 25 yrs to 31 yrs	
Child 11 yrs to 18 yrs Parents 32 yrs to 39 yrs	
Child 19 yrs to 39 yrs Parents 40 yrs to 60 yrs	
Child 40 yrs to 60 yrs Parents 61 yrs to 81 yrs	

Foundation GNVQ Health & Social Care © Hadfield, Towers and Wray, 1996. Published by Thomas Nelson & Sons Ltd.

 For more on development through the life stages, see pages 65 to 79.

Activity
Parenting

1 Choose some parents who you know well to talk to. They might be your own parents.

● Ask them how it felt when they first became parents and any changes that having a child brought to their lives.

● Make a list of the things they tell you. Some of the changes for the mother might be different from changes for the father.

● Highlight the changes that you think are positive in one colour, and the changes you think are negative in another colour.

2 In your group hold a discussion about being parents (parenting).

● What are the satisfying things, and the fun and exciting things? What are the more difficult things?

● Write down three good things about being a parent and three difficult things about being a parent.

Relationships at different life stages

Relationships in infancy

The main relationship at this life stage is between the baby and the mother figure (parent-child relationship). This gradually extends to the other parent, to other family members and those close to the family.

Relationships in childhood

The parent-child relationship continues strongly through this life stage, but in addition, the child starts to form friendships. At school, as the child becomes older, they form working relationships with others in the group.

Relationships in adolescence

The parent-child relationship changes, and friendships assume greater importance. Sexual relationships usually begin in adolescence. Working relationships form at school, college and sometimes in a job.

Relationships in adulthood

Adults continue their relationship with their own parents, but often become parents themselves, forming another parent-child relationship. Many adults have a sexual relationship, often a long term one, with one person. Friendships continue to be important, and working relationships form a large part of many adults' lives.

Relationships in old age

Although some elderly people are very socially active into their eighties and even nineties, for many elderly people relationships tend to be mostly with their family and close friends. The number of friends of the same age gets smaller as their friends die. This can have a negative effect on their self-esteem as they become closer to their own death. Families may be quite dependent on their older relatives: in some societies older people are seen as very wise, and they are relied upon for knowledge. Sometimes as older people become frail, physically and/or mentally, they may become dependent on family members or voluntary or paid carers.

All age groups in a family can be mutually supportive, helping each other in different ways, at different times. Often older people are very protective of their grandchildren, even if they have stopped being protective of their children.

What's so good about relationships?

Nearly everyone has a relationship with at least one other person, (usually many more), so there must be something good about them! At all stages in life, you can experience **positive relationships**.

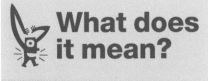

What does it mean?

- Positive relationship = a relationship where events, including difficult things, can be sorted out.

Activity
Good things

Make a chart like this:

Person I enjoy a relationship with	What makes it a positive relationship?
Boyfriend/girlfriend	S/he is kind to me I can be independent in this relationship I can be myself I feel safe S/he makes me laugh, we have fun
Parent/guardian/carer	

You don't have to use a boyfriend or girlfriend for your chart. Just list in the left hand column three people that you enjoy a relationship with. Write several things in the right-hand column about what makes it a positive relationship.

Discuss in a small group what you think this activity has shown you about the benefits of positive relationships. Make a list of them.

Why do relationships go wrong?

Sadly, many things can go wrong in a relationship in all sorts of ways. Here are a few examples:

- You like someone a lot, but they don't feel the same way.
- Someone at work really bosses you about.
- People in families are violent towards each other.
- Children experience a lot of arguing and fighting between their parents.
- Someone is not able to explain what they really mean – you get the wrong idea and feel hurt.
- A carer doesn't understand the needs of an older person – the older person get impatient and start shouting.
- You don't understand the needs of someone else fully – you try your best but get it wrong. They are cross and you feel guilty.
- A friend doesn't keep a secret.

Sometimes relationships go slightly wrong and things hurt for a short time, but are soon put right. Sometimes things are worse and it takes longer for the hurt to heal and for things to be put right. In some people's lives things go very badly wrong in relationships, sometimes for long periods of time. In these instances it may take years to heal the hurt, and specialist

For more on well-being, see page 32.

For more on self-esteem, see page 90.

help may be required. Relationships in which things are constantly wrong, causing people to be hurt a lot, are called **negative relationships**.

Positive and negative relationships affect your sense of **well-being**, your **self-esteem** and your development.

Activity
Family matters

Read the two case studies A and B.

Case study A
Chloe

Chloe is 6 years old and has been attending the local primary school for a year. Before that she was in the nursery class. She loves school and has lots of friends, many of whom live nearby. Nearly all of Chloe's friends are girls of the same age. They enjoy playing games together.

Chloe has an older sister Fiona, who is 10. Fiona sometimes gets a bit cross that Chloe always wants to play with her toys, but they usually get on really well and often give each other hugs and cuddles. Chloe's mum goes to work but is home in time to pick her up from school. Her dad has to work a little later, but nearly always gets home to help the two girls get ready for bed. Chloe likes this and always looks for her goodnight hug from her mum and dad. Although Chloe likes playing with her friends, she doesn't like to be away from her mum and dad at night times yet. She likes to know they are there when she wakes in the mornings.

The house has a small garden and there is a park nearby. On Saturdays Chloe goes to the park with her mum or dad, whichever one has not gone to do the shopping. Sometimes Fiona comes along too. Once a month all the family go to visit Granny and Grandpa who live in the city. These are Chloe's mum's parents. Chloe is always excited about seeing them because they give her more freedom than her mum and dad do. Chloe's other Grandad is dead now and her other Grandma lives in a nursing home because she had a really bad stroke. Sometimes Chloe's mum and dad take her to see Grandma. Chloe sits on her knee while Grandma tells her short stories.

1   Make notes on how you think Chloe's relationships with her family and friends, described in case study A, will affect her social and emotional development. You could use a chart like this.

Aspects of family life	Effects on Chloe
Loving sister	shows love learns to share

2   Discuss with two or three others in your group what you each thought about Chloe's relationships and the effects they had on her social and emotional development. You could record your discussions on audio tape.

● Let each person speak in turn without interruption and then each say what your views are about what the others have said.

● Discuss then describe what sort of person you think Chloe will grow up to be.

3   Think about and discuss how Chloe might grow up if she came from the family described in case study B.

You could also record this discussion.

Case study B

Chloe is 6 years old and attends the local primary school. Before that she was at nursery from the age of 12 months. She quite likes being at school because she likes painting, books and listening to stories; she doesn't have any paints or books at home. Chloe has three special friends and she always plays games with them at playtimes. She can't play with them after school because Chloe's 10 year old sister takes her home. They get the door key from a neighbour, but are not allowed to go out to play until their mum gets home. Often this is about 6.30 pm or 7 pm and Chloe's friends can't come to play at that time – Chloe's mum is usually tired and wants to get Chloe and Fiona to bed.

Chloe's dad doesn't usually get home until very late because he goes to the pub after work. Usually Chloe has gone to bed but she is often woken by her dad shouting loudly at her mum and she hears her mum crying. Chloe sleeps in the same bed as Fiona and she snuggles up to her sister when she hears her mum and dad arguing. Fiona is nice to Chloe and looks after her a lot.

4   When you think your discussion is finished, listen to your tape; see if anyone has anything else they want to add or change.

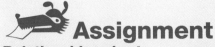 # Assignment
Relationships chart

Setting the scene

In this assignment you will produce a display with pictures and written information about the four types of relationship:

- parent-child relationships
- friendships
- working relationships
- sexual relationships.

The display should include brief case studies of relationships at each life stage

- 0 – 12 month old infant, and his/her mother (primary carer)
  child/parent relationship
- 2 girls or boys aged 7, 8 or 9 years
  friendship
- 2 teenagers, same sex, or different sex who work together
  working relationship
- married couple in their forties with children from 14 – 23 years
  sexual relationship and parent/child relationship
- 2 elderly people same sex or different sex who enjoy a social activity together
  friendship

Your display should include illustrations to show the relationships. Combine your work with others in the group, to make a larger display.

Note 1. Take care when choosing pictures to show sexual relationships. Do not use any pictures of people having sex; these can be embarrassing and sometimes offensive to others. If you have difficulty finding information about sexual relationships, you can talk with your teacher, and/or re-read the information on page 94.

You could collect pictures from magazines at home. You could have conversations with friends and family about relationships. Many programmes on television are about relationships, especially 'soaps', and these could give you some ideas for your activity. For example, your case study for working relationships could be two older teenagers with a part-time job on the market. You may also be able to gain experience of working relationships from a part-time job or work placement.

Note 2. To write a case study you need to use your imagination. It is rather like writing a short story. For a case study however, the content must be accurate. For example, if you are asked to write a case study about two friends who are eight years old, everything you say about eight year olds, their stage of development and friendships must be accurate. You would give the two friends names and write about things they like doing together and their friendship. When writing case studies use all the relevant information in the book. Look at the case studies in this book, to see how they have been written.

 For characteristics of relationships look at page 91. For more on life stages look at pages 66 to 79.

What kinds of relationships can you see in this scene?

Task 1

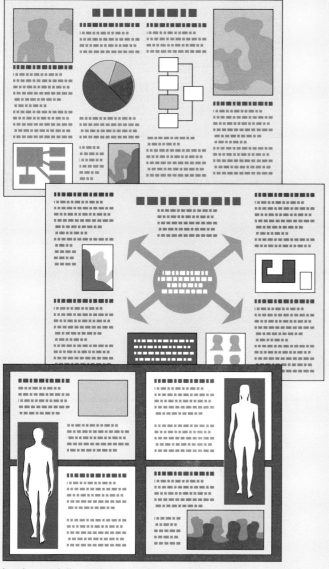

Look carefully at the description of the assignment above. Make a detailed plan of how you are going to make the display.

Task 2

Work carefully on writing your case studies and presenting your display. You could work with someone in your group. Use a word processor where possible.

Task 3

Write a short account of the benefits of positive relationships. Include this in your display and add your work from the activites on pages 97 and 98.

Task 4

Make two charts like these and complete them. You can include as many of each type as you wish, but you should fill in the positive relationships first. You should have at least one in each chart. Examples have been filled in for you.

Positive relationship with	The effect on my development
English teacher at senior school	I really began to enjoy English and understand it. I developed an interest in reading a number of different books. This helps me now to do my written work, and sometimes I know answers to questions because I have read about the subject. This has given me confidence and raised my self-esteem.

Negative relationship with	The effect on my development
An elderly woman who lived next door when I was at junior school	She used to shout whenever I went out to play. She used to say the ball might break her windows, and that me and my friends made too much noise. My mum would not let me play too far from the house and because I was frightened of the woman I used to stay in a lot. I did not get much fresh air or exercise and was shy at school for quite a long time.

Note: Do not use the *names* of anyone in the relationship column. This is important because of confidentiality. If you want to give an example from a present or recent relationship you should ask the person's permission.

Task 5

Put your display together.
When you have completed your display work think about:

- Do the colours and shapes look pleasing?
- Is the writing neat and easy to read? Could I use IT to make it look better?
- Have I included all four types of relationship?
- Does the work give the life stages during which these relationships usually happen?
- Has it explained something about each type of relationship?
- Has it described the benefits of positive relationships?

Ask yourself:

- Did I follow my plan? If not, why not?
- Would I do anything differently next time? If so, what?
- Could I have made it more interesting? How?

Opportunities to collect evidence

In this assignment you should cover:

Element 2.2
PCs 1, 2, 3, 4

Information Technology
Element 1.1, 1.2, 1.3

Communication
Element 1.1, 1.2, 1.3, 1.4

?Quiz

How much do you know about exploring relationships?

See page 155 for the answers.

Each question shows more than one possible answer, **a**, **b**, **c** and **d**; only one is correct.

1 Self-concept is *best* described as:
   a how you see yourself
   b what you think about yourself
   c the whole idea that you have about yourself
   d a , **b** and **c**

2 Friendship is one type of relationship. Which of these life stages is one where friendships are not formed?
   a adulthood
   b old age
   c infancy
   d adolescence

3 A combination of a friendship and strong physical attraction is often called a ...
   a negative relationship
   b romance
   c working relationship
   d an assertive relationship

4 Sharing, physical attraction, being protective, dependency and assertiveness are examples of:
   a names of life stages
   b characteristics of relationships
   c health and well-being
   d physical development

5 Dependency on another person can occur at any life stage, but which of the following is the stage where people are most dependent?
   a old age
   b adolescence
   c adulthood
   d infancy

6 Parents who get on really well with their child, and often give the child hugs and cuddles are most likely to help the child's:
   a emotional development
   b physical development
   c intellectual development
   d sensory development

7 (1) People in more senior jobs at work will sometimes use their position to have control and power over others.
   (2) When a person first starts work someone may look after them just until they settle in.
   (3) Someone looks after a new colleague at work, but continues to always protect them.

(4) Some people at work are very assertive and always get their own way.
Which of the following are *all* negative statements about working relationships.?
   a (1), (2) and (3)
   b (1), (2) and (4)
   c (1), (3) and (4)
   d (2), (3) and (4)

8 What do we call relationships that constantly go wrong and involve a lot of hurt?
   a positive
   b negative
   c formative
   d progressive

9 Which of these statements is true?
   a only good relationships can have an effect on our development
   b only bad relationships can have an effect on our development
   c relationships have no effect on our development
   d good and bad relationships can have an effect on our development

10 Which one of the following *best* describes a positive relationship?
   a a relationship in which both people are always happy
   b a relationship in which events, including difficult things can be sorted out
   c a relationship in which two people always agree with each other
   d a relationship in which there are many arguments which do not get sorted out

Scoring

If you got:
● between 1 and 4 – you are beginning to know something about relationships, but have some gaps. Go back over your work and talk to friends in your group and the teacher, and try the quiz again.
● between 5 and 8 – you are learning well and show that you know several things about relationships through life. Look up information for the questions you answered wrongly and try those ones again.
● between 9 and 10 – well done. You have learned a great deal about relationships. Now go on to learn about relationships between clients and carers.

Explore relationships between clients and carers

This element looks at the relationships between clients and carers, and builds on your knowledge of relationships in general.

By the end of the element, you should be able to:

describe what contributes to forming effective relationships between clients and carers

identify different needs of clients

explain ways in which clients' needs are met by carers

describe barriers to forming effective relationships between clients and carers

describe ways of overcoming barriers to forming effective relationships between clients and carers.

Making effective relationships

An **effective** relationship between you, the carer, and the person being helped (the client) is essential if you are to help and support others. The way you and your client interact with each other will have an important part to play in building this effective relationship. As a carer your clients could include children, elderly people and people with special needs.

 For more on the characteristics of relationships through the life stages, see pages 91 to 95.

What makes an effective relationship?

respect

recognition of individual identity

client choice

confidentiality

Respect

This means accepting someone for the person they are even if you do not like everything they do or everything they say, and your views are not the same as theirs. You should respect another person's way of life even if it is different from what you like, or think is right.

A carer's job is to help the client. The carer should always do this in a way that shows respect for the client. This means being considerate of the client's feelings and beliefs, and being honest, polite and kind. Treating the client like this will earn the carer the respect of the client, so that each person will be respecting the other. This is called mutual respect and is the basis for trust to develop between two people. The client needs the help of the carer and needs to be able to trust them.

Children as well as adults deserve respect. If children are shown respect they learn to respect others.

Recognition of individual identity

This means recognising each person as an individual. Each person is different to the next, if only slightly.

The activity **Alike and different** will have helped you to see yourself as an individual. You are unique, slightly different even from the person you think you are most like.

How can you show that you recognise a person's own individual identity?

- By finding out about the person's own likes and dislikes. For example some people like to go to bed early in the evening, others enjoy staying up later.
- By finding out what the person thinks about a situation. For example, when an event is on the news, some people might be very concerned about it, others might not think it was important
- By giving each person a choice, for example a choice of clothes or food
- By respecting a person's way of life, including their religion and beliefs
- By not thinking you know what someone wants better than they do
- By helping them to sort out problems in their own way
- By getting their agreement before you do things
- By helping people recognise what they can do for themselves. For example they may have difficulty peeling vegetables, but can put peeled potatoes in a pan, cover them with water, and place them on the cooker to boil
- By keeping private information confidential.

Activity
Alike and different

Working on your own, think of someone in your family that you think you are most like. Do not just think of physical likeness, but also similarities in your personality – the way you think about things and the activities you enjoy.

List all the ways in which you are alike and all the ways in which you are different.

Client choice

Offering clients choice is very important in treating them as an individual. To be able to make a choice they need to be given all the right information

It is important to remember choice when caring for children, too. Giving choices to children helps them to feel respected and helps them to develop their own sense of identity. The choices given to them need to be thought about carefully to make sure they are appropriate for their stage of development.

What would you like to wear today?

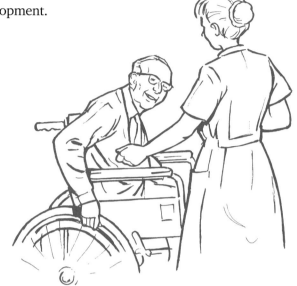

Where would you like to go today?

Activity
Children's choice

1   Copy and then complete the chart below by ticking either the Yes box or the No box to show whether you would give a choice in the these situations.

Age of child	Situation	Yes	No	Comments
1 years	Which toys to play with?			
2 years	When to cross the road?			
3 years	Whether or not to eat dinner?			
4 years	Which clothes to wear on a rainy day?			
5 years	Which book to borrow from the library?			
6 years	What to eat for breakfast?			
7 years	Which animal to have as a pet?			
8 years	What programme to watch on television?			
9 years	How to use their pocket money?			
10 years	How late to play out after tea?			

Foundation GNVQ Health & Social Care © Hadfield, Towers and Wray, 1996. Published by Thomas Nelson & Sons Ltd.

2   When you have completed the chart, talk with a partner about your decisions.

3   Have a discussion in your group about those decisions. Your tutor will want to join in the discussion. Talk about other situations you might come across where children should or should not be given a choice.

4   You will have found that deciding when and when not to give choices to children is quite difficult. It may be more complicated than a straightforward yes or no. Add points from your discussion to the comments box which would show this.

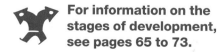

For information on the stages of development, see pages 65 to 73.

Confidentiality

As a carer you need to treat all that your client tells you, and all that you learn about them, with confidence; that is, not telling anyone else what you know about your client. At the start of the relationship, you must tell the client if there is any information that you will not be able to keep confidential. For example, a doctor would need to know about any changes in the client's condition. If it *is* necessary to pass on information, you need to tell the client why.

Because trust is part of the relationship developed between clients and carers, clients will often tell carers very personal information. They might say, 'Don't tell anyone will you?' In this case it is quite clear that this has been said in confidence. Clients will often talk openly to carers about personal things that they might not say to other people, because they trust them. If you disclose any of this information without the client's permission you are putting that trust at risk. Once trust is damaged it can be very difficult to restore.

Practical ways of setting up and keeping an effective relationship

Hello Elsie, how are you today?

- Greet the client with a smile, and a welcoming statement that shows you are interested.

● Listen carefully to clients when they talk.

Show you are giving attention by maintaining eye contact, and nodding occasionally. Sometimes people say 'Mm', as people tell them something. These little gestures help to show genuine interest. Find time to sit down and listen fully, rather than hoping you can listen whilst you are doing something else. The client will know if you are really interested.

● Find out what the client likes to be called.

Some clients are formal and like to be called by a title and surname. Others prefer their first name and some even like their nickname. Always use the client's name, don't use endearments like 'love' or 'sweetie'.

● Always be there at the times you said you would.

If something out of your control has happened, always try to let the client know that you will be late or not be there. Keep other promises too. If you have said you will take something to or get something for the client, remember to do so.

If you do not do these things you may form **barriers**.

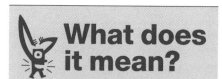

What does it mean?

● **Barriers = something which gets in the way and prevents a good relationship.**

Barriers to effective relationships

Barriers include:

- **lack of respect**
- **insufficient time to devote to clients**
- **aggressiveness**
- **not respecting confidentiality.**

 Can you think of more?

Ways of breaking down barriers

- Enable clients to do things to help themselves.
  Doing too much for a client can create just as big a barrier in the relationship as doing too little.
- Be patient and understanding.
  A client needs care. This is because they have some illness, disability or other problem and may be in discomfort, pain or distress. All these can cause a client to be grumpy or even angry. It can seem as though the client is angry with the carer. This is especially true if the client does not see many other people.
- Always try to be calm.
  A client may be angry, but returning anger with anger will create a barrier in the relationship. Try to assess what is causing the anger, but don't insist on a reason; sometimes the client may not know. Often the anger will not be about the carer at all, but something entirely different. For example, a client can become angry because they are lonely.
- Be honest with your client.
  If the reason for a client's anger is something that you have done or not done, then be honest, apologise and try to put things right, or make sure not to make the same mistake again. Be honest in other situations too. For example, if you have forgotten something, say so.
- Take care of yourself.
  You, as a carer, can get tired and frustrated. Take time off to rest and do things you enjoy. Be sure there is someone who will care for you. It can be helpful to tell someone about the difficulties of a carer's job. You could tell your supervisor or manager, but sometimes you may want to talk to someone outside the job, but remember **confidentiality**.
- Try not to be too busy.
  Rushing around doing things *for* the client can mean that there is little or no time to be *with* the client. If the client thinks the carer is very busy, this might prevent the client from talking to the carer.

For more on confidentiality see page 106.

Carers

Not all carers are professionals like nurses, care assistants, social workers and doctors. They can be family members, such as a mother who looks after a child, or a relative caring for an older person. Some carers are voluntary workers, unpaid carers, for organisations such as Age Concern or MIND. All carers, whether trained or not, try to meet the needs of clients.

The needs of clients

These needs can be grouped as:

- physical
- intellectual
- emotional
- social.

(Social needs can vary greatly according to a person's cultural background.)
You grow and develop:

- physically – and have needs like the need for food, and to keep warm
- intellectually – and have the need for your mind to be stimulated
- emotionally – and have needs to express feelings and to be accepted by others
- socially – and have needs for other people to interact with, as individuals and in groups.

When studying development you learned that each area of development overlapped. This is true, also, of needs. You can have more than one need at any one time, though it may sometimes seem important to give more attention to certain needs than to others.

Meeting needs

There are different ideas on how people get their needs met, and how people can be *helped* to get their needs met. The main work of a carer is to help meet the needs of clients. One idea about meeting needs is that the physical needs for food, water and shelter are the most basic and should to be met first. These are closely followed by the emotional need to be free from fear and danger. Once these two levels of need have been met, people need to love and be loved.

The idea is that basic needs will usually be considered first. For example, someone who does not have enough money to pay for food and rent will try to solve this problem first before they think about their lack of social life.

In what ways can carers help meet client's needs?

Remember that the client knows their own needs best. However, they may not always be able to tell you their needs. For example, a young baby or someone who cannot speak properly after a stroke will not be able to communicate in words.

When a person has lost some of their independence it is usual for them to need a carer. This is because they have lost their ability to meet some of their needs themselves and so need help. Many things can happen in your

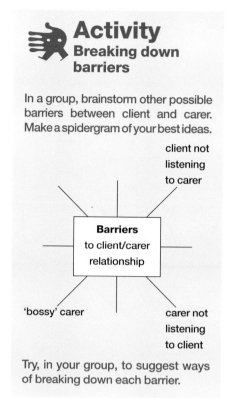

Activity
Breaking down barriers

In a group, brainstorm other possible barriers between client and carer. Make a spidergram of your best ideas.

client not listening to carer

Barriers
to client/carer relationship

'bossy' carer

carer not listening to client

Try, in your group, to suggest ways of breaking down each barrier.

For more on needs, see pages 44 to 46 and 110 to 112.

life which could cause you to become more dependent on others. Sometimes this is temporary, for example a broken arm, sometimes it is permanent, for example paralysis following an accident.

How are these clients needs being met?

Whatever the needs of a client, the carer may have to help with some or all of:

- **feeding**
- **dressing**
- **personal hygiene**.

Feeding

Young babies soon learn to feed themselves. It is something you do independently for many years, and so it can feel very awkward and embarassing to be fed by someone.

Activity
What does it feel like to be fed?

1. Work with a partner in the group. Decide on a food that you each like and which is easy to bring into school or college, and does not need any preparation, for example yogurt.

2. Plan a time for feeding each other, and at the planned time bring the food and the right cutlery and crockery.

3. Prepare your partner for their 'meal'. Remember to tell them what it is, to ask them if they want to eat, and whether they want this particular food.

4. Prepare the environment, for example table, chairs, table mat, napkins, etc. and put the food into the right crockery.

5. Feed your client, remembering to talk to them appropriately.

6. Clear away, and then allow your partner to carry out the same activity with you.

7. Discuss with your partner how it felt to be fed by someone. What did your partner/carer do that was alright for you? What things irritated you or made you feel embarassed? Did it feel awkward? What did you want to do yourself?

8. Make some notes about what it felt like to be helped with your food.

Even if a client needs help they may not actually need feeding. They may need help to prepare the meal, but can eat it themselves. They may need help to know what the meal is and what is where on the plate if they have very poor eyesight. They may just need special cutlery and can then feed themselves, for example people with severe arthritis. Remember to let clients choose what they want to eat.

Dressing

Dressing yourself is quite complicated. There are many movements involved and a great deal of coordination. Imagine having a broken arm, and trying to put on a blouse or a shirt and fasten the buttons.

You need to be sensitive about how someone might feel when you are helping them to dress. Most people feel quite embarassed about someone, especially someone they do not know well, seeing them with few or no clothes on. Very young children do not usually mind so much, but are usually eager to dress themselves. They can become very frustrated if they are unable to do what they usually do. You need to let people choose what they want to wear.

Personal hygiene

This means helping someone keep themselves clean. This can be by washing, bathing or showering. Again, you need to allow people to choose whatever method they can manage. Some older people are not used to having a bath or shower, and prefer to wash to keep clean. This is perfectly adequate as long as it is done regularly.

You need to be sensitive about other people's feelings when they need help with personal hygiene. Hair care, nail care, teeth and mouth care are all important. Sometimes people will need help with the laundering of their clothes, so that they always have something fresh to wear. Clean underwear is needed every day.

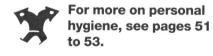 **For more on personal hygiene, see pages 51 to 53.**

Take an interest in the client

It can create a barrier to your relationship if what you are doing with the client appears to be 'just a job'. You can do this by chatting to them and finding out more about them. This shows you are interested in them as a person.

Communicate effectively with the client

You need to talk to the client appropriately. Think about their age – children need a different approach from elderly people. Just because a person is disabled in some way, perhaps using a wheelchair, it does not mean that they cannot make sense of what you say.

 For information about language development in children, see pages 67, 70, 71, 72.

Provide information

Clients should be told what you are doing to help care for them. For example you may explain why you are changing a dressing on a wound. This will help to involve the client in the process. They should be told when to expect a visit from you and if any other carers are coming in the next few days. It is important to keep them informed.

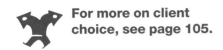

For more on client choice, see page 105.

Encourage choice

Encouraging choice forms the basis of a positive relationship between the client and the carer. To make choices the client needs information. If you are unsure about what information should be given to a client, you should check with a more senior carer. You should always give a client information about what you are doing.

Enable independence

Always check what clients can do for themselves before you do it for them. Sometimes, your own need to feel needed can take priority and you do something that the client could do for themselves. Sometimes, a client has become used to having something done for them and doesn't recognise that they could do it for themselves.

Carers can help clients to recognise what they can do for themselves and then help them to achieve it. For example, a client may have become used to having meals prepared for them, but be capable of preparing their own with encouragement. Doing something independently can raise a client's self-esteem and provide a stimulating challenge.

Being independent can meet physical, intellectual, emotional and social needs. For example, helping someone to become more mobile will improve their physical health and meet their need to get from place to place. It could help to meet their social and intellectual needs. They might meet new people who could give them more emotional support.

Recognise cultural differences

A carer should always respect the cultural differences of their clients. A client's cultural background can make a difference to their needs and/or the way in which the needs might be met. For example, different religious beliefs may bring different dietary needs – a very strict Christian will not eat meat on Fridays.

Different religious beliefs might also bring different needs when a person is ill or dying. For example, in the Jewish faith the tradition is for a loved one to remain with the dying person until death occurs.

Different cultures have different hygiene needs and patterns. For example, for a Muslim, the left hand is considered a dirty hand and things considered unclean can only be done with that hand.

As a carer, you cannot be expected to know all the cultural differences which may relate to your clients. If you are unsure, it is best to ask the client in a sensitive way what you need to know. Explain that you want to help them in a way that is right for them, so that you can care for them in the best way.

If the client cannot communicate with you adequately, ask them if you can speak to a relative or friend. Another carer may be able to give you information about different traditions and beliefs.

Activity
Help to be mobile

1   In your whole group, brainstorm ideas of aids that can help people become more mobile.
2   Make a spidergram of your ideas.

Activity
Caring for older people

With the other members of your group look at these descriptions of five older people in Greenbanks Residential Home.

Case studies

Alice: is 90 years old and has lived in the residential home for eight years since her husband died. She has very little sight and some trouble hearing properly, but she can get about and is still very sharp-minded. Her only son, Ronald, visits her every week.

Elsie: is 83 years old and has lived in the home for five years. She has never been married, but has always been close to her sister, Beatrice, who is 81. Elsie has very severe arthritis, which makes it difficult for her to do many daily living activities. Beatrice has not been able to visit Elsie during the last three months because she had a fall and broke her hip, and still feels afraid of going out of the house.

Tom: is 79 years old and has only recently come to live in the home after suffering a stroke. The stroke left him paralysed down the right side of his body, and he now has difficulties in speaking and swallowing. Tom's wife died ten years ago, but his two daughters and their families have been to visit Tom frequently since he came to the home.

Sabia: is 89 years old and is in the home for 2 months. She lives with her daughter and her family since her own husband died. Her daughter and her family have gone to visit relatives in India, but Sabia could not go because she is too frail for the journey. She has very poor eyesight and is weak on her left side because she had a mild stroke. Sabia is Muslim and speaks almost no English. Her son and family, who live a long distance away, are coming to see Sabia next weekend.

Ted: is 80 years old and has been at the home for three years. He was becoming increasingly confused, and his wife, Annie, felt unable to look after him any longer on her own. Although Ted's wife visits three times a week he does not really know who she is. Ted often wets or soils himself because he doesn't realise he is not at the toilet. Sometimes he gets angry at the carers, and asks them what they are doing in his house.

Make a chart of the five clients and their needs and suggest who could meet them and how. This has been completed for Alice – complete the others.

Client	Need(s)	How they could be met	By whom
Alice	to get about safely	spectacles white stick	optician Social Services
	to hear better	hearing aid to be spoken to clearly and at a steady pace	family doctor by all people who are in contact with her, including carers
	company	day centre volunteer visitors	Social Services, church carers, family, friends
	intellectual stimulation	conversation radio	all carers, family and friends bought by self or family, or provided by the home

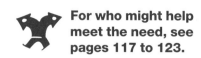

For who might help meet the need, see pages 117 to 123.

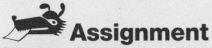

Assignment

Clients and carers

Setting the scene

For each of the following tasks
a) in groups of 3 or 4, discuss the questions posed
b) write up your own answers to the questions.

Case study

Joanna

Joanna is 4½ years old and has just started school. She has only attended for 4 days and is still a little upset when her Mum leaves her, even though she went to playgroup for two years. Joanna is usually a chatty little girl and likes playing with other children, but she has been rather quiet during these first few days at school.

Joanna is within the normal range of development for all aspects of her development. Once she has been helped to make the adjustment of going to school she will probably settle down and enjoy school.

Task 1

What will Joanna's teacher need to do to build a positive relationship with her?

For more on the normal range of development, see page 71. For more on client-carer relationships, see pages 103 to 107. For more on the characteristics of relationships, see page 91.

Task 2

What barriers could there be in the relationship between Joanna and her teacher that might prevent Joanna settling down well at school? If these barriers develop, how could they be overcome?

Task 3

How could Joanna's teacher overcome any barriers?

Task 4

What do you think Joanna's needs are?

Task 5

How can Joanna's teacher help to meet Joanna's needs while she is at school?

For more on the physical, intellectual, emotional and social development of a 4–5 year old, see page 71. For more on the barriers to a relationship and ways of overcoming them, see page 108.

Case study

Sadik

Sadik is 19 years old, and until his motorbike accident three months ago, was very active. As well as biking, he enjoyed sports such as football, swimming and basketball. He has two brothers, one 17 and one 21, and a sister aged 22. His sister is married, but Sadik and his brothers still live at home with their mother and father.

Sadik is in the second year of an Advanced Business Administration Course at college. Sadik's injuries from his accident were very severe, and at first the doctors thought he would be completely paralysed from the neck down. However, during the last six weeks at rehabilitation hospital the feeling and movement has started to come back to Sadik's arms, but not enough to completely feed or dress himself. Both legs remain totally paralysed and he does not have total control of his bladder or bowel.

There are a number of other young people around Sadik's age at the rehabilitation hospital. There are many people involved in Sadik's care but he has one nurse who looks after him a lot of the time. She is his **named nurse** or **keyworker**.

Task 5

Since Sadik has been in the rehabilitation hospital what might his named nurse have done in order to build a positive and effective relationship with him?

Task 6

What things could form barriers to a positive relationship between Sadik and his named nurse? If these things became barriers how could they be overcome?

Task 7

What are Sadik's main needs?

Task 8

How can his carers help to meet his needs?

For more on making effective relationships between clients and carers, see pages 103 to 107.

To help you work out some of Sadik's needs, see the discussion of adolescent and adult development on pages 74 to 77.

Opportunities to collect evidence

In this assignment you should cover:

Element 2.3
PCs 1, 2, 3, 4

Communication
Element 1.1, 1.2, 1.4

?Quiz

How much do you know about exploring relationships between client and carer?

See page 155 for the answers.

Each question shows more than one possible answer, **a**, **b**, **c** and **d**; only one is correct.

1 Which of these is the most accurate description of an effective relationship between client and carer?
   a One where the client is always happy
   b One in which the client's needs are met appropriately
   c One in which the carer enjoys his/her job
   d One in which the client's relatives are involved

2 Which of these is not essential in order to build an effective relationship between client and carer?
   a respect
   b confidentiality
   c happiness
   d choice

3 Mutual respect means:
   a the client respecting the carer
   b the client and carer respecting each other
   c the carer respecting the client
   d the carer respecting the client's family

4 Who knows best what a client's needs are?
   a the doctor
   b the client
   c the relative
   d the social worker

5 Which of these clients would be most likely *not* to be able to tell you their needs?
   a A four year old within the normal range of development
   b An elderly person who is in good health
   c A one year old within the normal range of development
   d A teenage boy who uses a wheelchair because his legs are paralysed

6 Which of these is the most accurate description of confidentiality between client and carer?
   a The carer not telling anyone anything about the client
   b The carer only telling some people the things she thinks need to be told about the client
   c The carer only telling others those things that carer and client have agreed will be told to others
   d The carer only telling the doctor about the client

7 Which one of the following would help most to maintain a positive relationship between client and carer?
   a Giving messages to the relatives
   b Doing everything the client wants
   c Keeping promises made to the client
   d Collecting prescriptions from the doctor

8 Which one of the following would be most likely to create a barrier in the relationship between the carer and the client?
   a Not understanding straight away what the client needed
   b The carer being tired and getting cross with the client
   c The carer telling the client that she would not be able to come to her tomorrow
   d The carer encouraging the client to sort out their own problems

9 A physically disabled client needs assistance getting in and out of the bath, and a lifting hoist is used. The carer explains to the client how the hoist is to be used. The main reason for this explanation is because:
   a clients always need to be told what to do
   b the law requires the carer to do so
   c it will save time
   d it involves the client in the process of care

10 Which of the following is a **most** important factor for a carer to remember about his/her client?
   a what age they are
   b whether they are male or female
   c that they are all individuals
   d their home phone number

Scoring

If you got:

● between 1 and 4 – you are beginning to learn about the relationship between clients and carers and about client needs and meeting them. There are still some gaps in your knowledge, though, and you need to go over your work, talk with others in the group and your teacher and try the quiz again.

● between 5 and 8 – you are learning well and understanding quite a lot about caring for others. Look up information for the questions you answered wrongly and try them again. Check with your teacher for things you do not understand.

● 9 or 10 – Well done, you are showing a good knowledge of meeting the needs of others.

Unit 3

Investigate working in health and social care

This unit looks at the services involved in providing different types of care for people of all ages. It will help you to:

- learn what skills and qualities you need for a particular job in the caring services
- decide on a job or career when you leave school or college.

Investigate working in health and social care services in the UK

In this element you will learn about the main types of health and social care and who provides that health and social care. You will also be looking at the main purposes of job roles in each different type of care. By the end of this element you should be able to:

- identify the main providers of health and social care and give examples of the main types of service they provide
- describe and give the main purpose of job roles in health and medical care
- describe and give the main purpose of job roles in community care and support
- identify and give the main purpose of job roles in indirect care.

Who provides health care?

The main providers of health and social care are:

- **National Health Service (NHS)** – funded from the taxes and national insurance we pay from our salaries
- **Social Services** – funded from the taxes and national insurance we pay from our salaries
- **Private sector** – paid for directly by the client
- **Voluntary sector** – funded from donations of money or time, often organised through charities.

National Health Service and Social Services

The NHS and Social Services are part of the welfare system set up in 1948 to care for people 'from the cradle to the grave'. The NHS provides most of the health and medical care in Britain. It provides people with medical, nursing and hospital care and treatment. The NHS is one of the largest employers in Britain and offers a very wide variety of jobs.

The 1990 NHS and Community Care Act introduced many changes to health care. The aim of the act was to care for more people in residential accommodation in the community or in their own homes.

How is statutory care provided?

Statutory care is provided by the NHS:

- at your doctor's surgery or local health clinic or centre.

This is where people usually come to first for health care.

- in hospital.

  You may be referred here by your doctor for treatment as an **outpatient** or as an **inpatient**. You can also admit yourself for treatment to the Accident and Emergency Department. Some larger hospitals provide specialist care, for example, heart surgery and kidney dialysis.

- in your own home.

Various health care professionals are able to visit, treat and care for you in your own home. They include the doctor, district or community nurse or midwife, care assistant, chiropodist, occupational therapist and physiotherapist.

What does it mean?

- Sector = section.

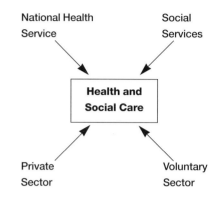

What do they mean?

- Outpatient = a person who goes to a hospital or clinic for treatment or an operation and goes home the same day.

- Inpatient = a person who stays overnight in a hospital.

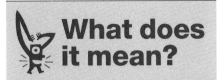

What does it mean?

- **Statutory service = a service that has been set up by law. Statutory services include the health (under the NHS) and Social Services.**

Activity
My area

In a group photocopy part of a map of your local area. You should include the nearest town if you live outside one. Draw a large circle around the town centre. Using local sources of information, find the places within this circle where health care and social care services are provided by the state. (You may find that some provide private care as well.) Find at least **four** types of service. Put them on your map, using a key and symbols.

Symbols you could use for your map.

Social Services care

A variety of social care and support is provided by the social services and, like the NHS, it is a **statutory service**. There have been changes in the care provided by the social services. For example, elderly people now have to contribute more money towards their care. Fewer people are now cared for in residential care homes. Instead people get help to enable them to stay in their own homes. This change puts greater demands on voluntary organisations and local communities.

How is social care provided?

Social care is provided:

- in residential care homes for the elderly
- in a client's own home
- in family centres
- in day nurseries
- in day centres for the elderly
- in residential homes for people with learning difficulties or special needs
- in hostels for people with mental health problems.

Private care

Some people decide to pay for their own care either from their savings or from an insurance scheme that they pay into over a number of years. Sometimes health insurance, such as BUPA, is provided by an employer. If you use the private sector you may not have to wait very long for treatment and you can choose appointment times to suit you.

How is private care provided?

Private care is provided:

- by specialist doctors in private consulting rooms
- in private hospitals and clinics
- by health **professionals** such as physiotherapists or osteopaths in private rooms or clinics or in your own home
- in residential care homes or nursing homes.

What does it mean?

- **Professional = a specialist in a particular occupation who has been trained. Doctors, nurses and physiotherapists are health professionals.**

Activity
Local services

Look in the *Yellow Pages* and your local newspaper to find out which private health services and social care services are provided in your area. Find **four** examples of each type of service. Mark these on the map you used in the activity **My area**.

Voluntary care

The voluntary sector consists of a large number of organisations providing a wide variety of care. Age Concern, Mencap and the NSPCC are examples. The services provided range from full-time home and residential care to part-time day care. This could be a weekly visit for a friendly chat or to do the shopping for example.

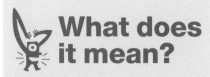

What does it mean?

● **Respite care = giving the permanent carer a break, whilst the client is looked after in their own home or in hospital/residential accommodation.**

Activity
Local voluntary services

Find at least **four** voluntary organisations in your area and mark them on the map you made in the activity **My area**. To help you do this you could visit your local library or Citizens Advice Bureau or ask your tutor to arrange for someone from the organisation to come and talk to your group.

Activity
See for yourself

With the help of your supervisor, arrange a visit to one of the voluntary service organisations you have identified and ask about the types of service it provides and the roles involved.

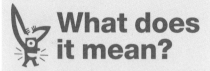

What does it mean?

● **Indirect care = jobs that support the delivery of care to clients e.g. porters, catering staff in hospitals; receptionists, caretakers in health centres.**

For more on indirect care, see page 128.

How is voluntary care provided?

Voluntary care is provided in:

● day centres
● client's own home
● youth clubs
● holiday homes
● **respite care** for relatives
● residential homes for people with various disabilities
● information centres, for example a Citizens Advice Bureau
● practical support, for example Volunteer Bureaux.

Community services

People can be cared for in their own homes by the community services. These are provided by the three sectors:

● state
● private
● voluntary.

People may receive either:

● direct care
● **indirect care**
● health and medical care
  or a mixture of all three.

Case study

Jenny's accident

Last week six-year old Jenny, was taken by ambulance to the Accident and Emergency Department of her local hospital because she broke her arm when she fell off the swing at playschool. Her great-grandmother is in the Care of the Elderly Unit at the same hospital because she has a chest infection. When Jenny went to visit her, she bought Jenny some sweets from the hospital trolley – run by voluntary workers. Jenny's dad has also been unlucky as he hurt his back at work two weeks ago and he paid to see a physiotherapist about it. It is a busy time as Jenny's mum will be visited by a social worker next week because she is hoping to become a **foster parent.**

Jenny's family is receiving care from several sectors:

NHS
- Jenny goes to the Accident and Emergency Department with a broken arm.
- Jenny's father asks his doctor for written permission to see a physiotherapist for treatment to his back.
- Jenny's great-grandmother is in the Care of the Elderly Unit in hospital.

Social Services
- Jenny's mother will discuss being a foster parent with Social Services.

Private
- Jenny's father pays to see a physiotherapist for treatment to his back.

Voluntary
- Jenny's great-grandmother is able to buy sweets and toiletries from the hospital trolley staffed by the WRVS (Women's Royal Voluntary Service).

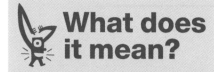

What does it mean?

- Foster parent = someone who looks after children for periods of time in their own home, including overnight, and treats them like their own children.

Activity
Care providers and jobs available

Cut out newspaper advertisements for jobs in the NHS, Social Services, private sector and voluntary sector. You could look in local and national newspapers (including local free papers, Wednesday's copy of *The Guardian*, *Community Care,* and *Nursing Times.* You can find these in the library or local Social Services office). For each of the four sectors find at least **four** advertisements. Display the advertisements to show the provider and the service; you could use one piece of paper for each. Put headings on your sheets.

NHS

RGN required for busy surgical ward. Apply with details of employment history to: Mr C.V. Thornley, Personnel, Frimley General Hospital, Frimley, FG6 2LQ

Social Services

Care assistants for night duty in Oakleigh Residential Home. Please telephone: Ruffield 01238 – 111789.

Private

Registered General Nurse (RGN). Qualified nursing staff required for full-time or part-time day duties in Private Nursing Home. Excellent conditions and good rates of pay. PHONE MRS FOSTER ON: ECKENHAM 01666 – 997432

RELIABLE PERSON REQUIRED as child minder/nanny. Framston area. 2 children, 11 and 9, to pick up from school and supervise. Approx 3.30 pm until 8.00 pm. 5 days a week. Tel: 01605 – 434591

Experienced cook required for rest home. Competitive salary. Please contact Mr Butler on Shilcot 01386 – 218494

Voluntary

Volunteer required for Oxfam Shop. Apply to the Manageress, Mrs K. Pearson, 406 Albert Road, Coldwell. Please supply 2 references.

Job roles in health and medical care

Health and medical care is provided by highly trained staff such as doctors, nurses, dentists and opticians who work closely together.

The job roles include:

- **Family doctor** (General Practitioner or GP)
  - will **diagnose** diseases, assess injuries
  - gives health advice
  - treats some conditions
  - writes prescriptions
  - refers patients to hospital for specialist care

  Qualification – 5 years and 1 year as House Doctor in a hospital plus 3 years GP training

  Need – to be calm, tolerant and understanding
  to keep aware of new research

- **Midwife**
  - delivers babies
  - works in the community or hospital
  - carries out ante-natal and post-natal checks
  - carries out other procedures that RGNs and community nurses do

  Qualification – 3 years to become a RGN and 18 months to become Registered Midwife

  Need – to be encouraging, calm and kind
  to have good practical skills and pay attention to detail

- **Nurse** (Registered General Nurse RGN)
  - works in NHS, private hospital or nursing home
  - assesses and gives care and treatment
  - carries out tests and observation
  - works in a team or supervises a team

  Qualification – 3 years – Project 2000 for Diploma plus RGN or approx 4 years for degree plus RGN

  Need – to be accurate and pay attention to detail
  to have tolerance, patience and kindness

- **Practice nurse** (Registered General Nurse)
  - gives injections, carries out blood tests
  - gives advice on care
  - works closely with a doctor in the surgery or health centre

  Qualification – Same as for RGN above but a different place of work

  Need – to work as part of a team
  to be a good communicator
  same skills as an RGN

- **District** or **Community nurse**
  - assesses the needs of the client in the community
  - gives injections and dresses wounds
  - visits the client at home
  - supervises a team of home carers

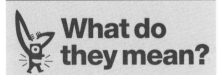

What does it mean?

- **Diagnose = find out what is wrong with a patient – called 'making a diagnosis'.**

What do they mean?

- **Ante-natal = before a baby is born.**

- **Post-natal = after a baby is born.**

Qualification – RGN and 38 weeks additional training

Need –to be able to work on own initiative

to be patient and understanding

● **Health visitor**

– advise and educate people on health matters

– checks children's health up to school age

– helps parents whose children have feeding or behavioural problems

– works closely with a doctor at a surgery or health clinic

– visits clients at home

Qualification – RGN and additional training

Need – to be patient and very understanding

to be good at helping people solve their problems

● **Dentist**

– examines patient's mouth and teeth

– carries out X-rays and gives treatment

– gives advice on tooth care

– fits new teeth

Qualification – 5 year degree in Dentistry and 1 year vocational training

Need – to have practical skills/ a steady hand

to have a sympathetic nature and good communication skills

● **Optician (optometrist)**

– works in hospital, private practice or for a lens manufacturer

– examines people's eyesight

– diagnoses diseases or need for glasses

– prescribes glasses

Qualification – 3 year degree and 1 year as a trainee plus Part II exams

Need – to have good observational skills

to be very accurate, paying attention to detail

● **Physiotherapist**

– works in NHS or private practice

– assesses need for treatment e.g. exercises, manipulation, massage

– carries out treatment/exercises for people whose movement is restricted

by injury, illness or age

– helps client to improve muscle strength and movement

Qualification – 3 year degree

Need – to be patient and help clients persevere

to work as a team member

● **Occupational therapist** (OT)

– works closely with doctors, nurses and physiotherapists to help people

with physical or mental problems or who are mentally ill

– assesses client in hospital/home

– prescribes aids to make client's lives easier, for example wheelchair,

bath hoist, activities

Qualification – 3 year degree

Need – to be good at problem solving

to help clients become as independent as possible

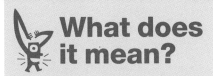

What does it mean?

- **Ultrasound scan** = Use of sound waves to produce an image, it is sometimes used instead of an X-ray.

For more on qualifications, see pages 137 to 139.

What does it mean?

- **Diagnostic** = using various tests and machinery to find out if a person has an illness or disease.

What do they mean?

- **Remedial care** = helping to restore to normal activity.
- **Therapeutic** = something that makes you feel better mentally as well as physically.

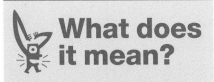

What does it mean?

- **Dietitian** = a person whose job it is to make sure that a person's food intake is well-balanced.

● **Diagnostic radiographer**
  – works with doctors/nurses in hospital department or on a ward
  – assesses client for X-ray
  – carry out X-ray
  – carries out other procedures, for example, **ultrasound scan**.
  Qualification – 3 year degree
  Need – to have good communication skills
          to be very accurate, paying attention to detail

● **Pharmacist**
  – may work in a hospital, high street chemist or in industry
  – have a high standard of academic knowledge
  – labels and gives out medicines
  – works in a team with others
  Qualification – 3 year degree plus pre-registration year to become
                  Registered Pharmacist
  Need – to be extremely accurate
         to be good at communicating instructions to staff and the public

What are the main purposes of job roles in health and medical care?

Diagnostic care

The purpose of a doctor's job is to examine patients and make a medical diagnosis. The doctor may order a blood test, scan, X-ray or ECG (electro-cardiograph) to help with the diagnosis. These tests are carried out by other health workers whose job it is to carry out **diagnostic** care. Examples of these health workers include radiographers and cardiological technicians.

Health maintenance

Some jobs in health and medical care, for example health visitors, are concerned with health maintenance. Health visitors see families with young children to check that they are developing normally and that they are following immunisation schedules.

Remedial and therapeutic care

Some health professionals, for example physiotherapists and occupational therapists, are involved with **remedial** and **therapeutic care**. They help patients recover from disease or injury by giving them special exercises or treatments.

Education of clients

Some jobs include educational purposes. Clients are given information that enables them to lead a healthier lifestyle and be free from illness and disease. If you become a health visitor, health promotion officer, **dietitian**, community midwife, nurse or doctor, this will be part of your job.

Activity
Match them up

Match the picture to the words.

a
patient
blood technician
syringes/needles/swabs
bottles

b
radiographer
X-ray machine
patient

c
pathology laboratory
technician/worker
microscope
slides/blood/bottles
machinery

d
crutches
patient
physiotherapist

e
thermometer, equipment
  for blood pressure
nurse
patient

f
health visitor
mother/child
case notes/weighing scales

g
nurse
patient
doctor

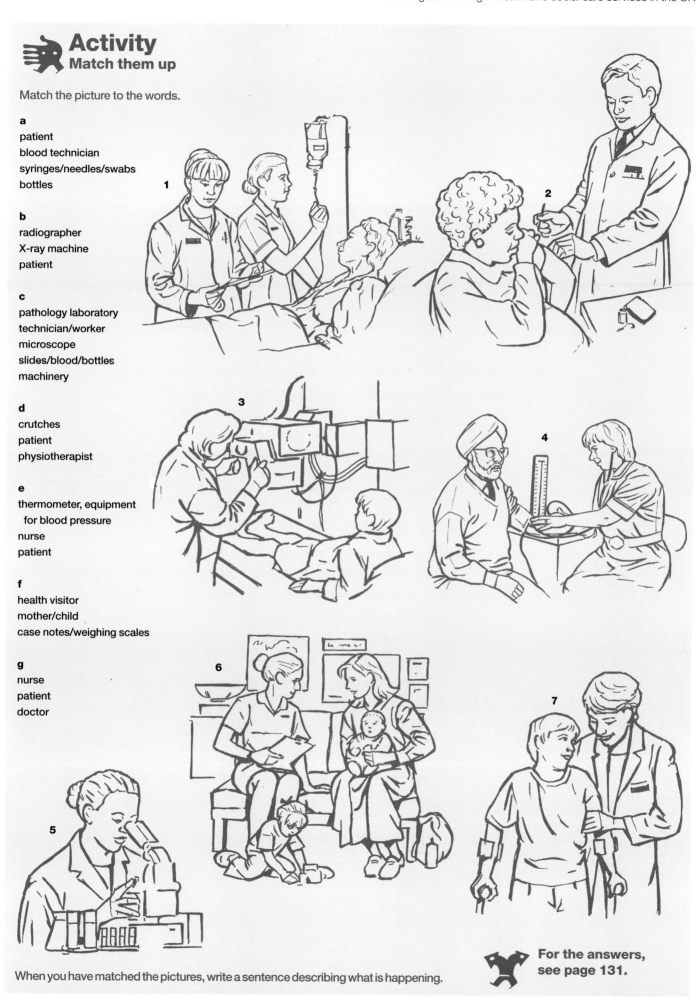

When you have matched the pictures, write a sentence describing what is happening.

For the answers, see page 131.

Job roles in community care and support

In many care jobs, it is part of the role to give emotional care and support, as well as doing physical care tasks such as bathing a client. Clients can also be helped with difficult problems and decisions. Care and support can be provided on a full- or part-time basis in day centres, residential homes or the client's own home. Much care is provided by relatives. Carers need support, too, and this is provided, for example, by Crossroads, a voluntary organisation. They will provide care in the home to give the carer a break.

The job roles include:

● **Social worker**
   - provides emotional and social support for clients with problems
   - helps find accommodation and direct clients to other types of support
   - works in residential care and day care for children, adults and elderly people
   - works with physically and mentally handicapped people
   - works with people with mental health problems

Qualification – 2 year Diploma in Social Work

Need – to be mature, sensible and stable
          to be tolerant and understanding

● **Care work assistant**
   - works in day centres and residential homes for elderly people or the client's home
   - works to a care plan set down by experienced staff
   - helps clients with daily activities such as bathing and dressing
   - serves meals and feed clients if necessary
   - carries out general household tasks
      (Care work assistants sometimes have a different job title when they work in a hospital setting, for example auxiliary nurses or health care assistants.)

Qualification – none necessary, can achieve NVQs in Direct Care

Need – to be able to use common sense and initiative
          to be kind, tolerant and understanding

● **Nursery nurse/nanny**
   - work in client's home (nanny), state or private nursery (nursery nurse)
   - may work in a team or alone to provide child care
   - help children to learn through play and keep them safe
   - help children to learn acceptable behaviour
   - may make snacks/meals, carry out light duties around the nursery or home

Qualification – 2 year Diploma in Nursery Nursing (DNN) or NVQ's in Childcare and Education

Need – to work closely with others satisfying the needs of children
          to have creative skills

● Child minder

– looks after children in their own home

– carries out the same tasks as parents

– assessed by Social Services.

Qualification – registered by Social Services

Need – to be calm and patient

to be good at dealing with children

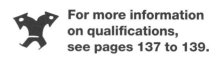

For more information on qualifications, see pages 137 to 139.

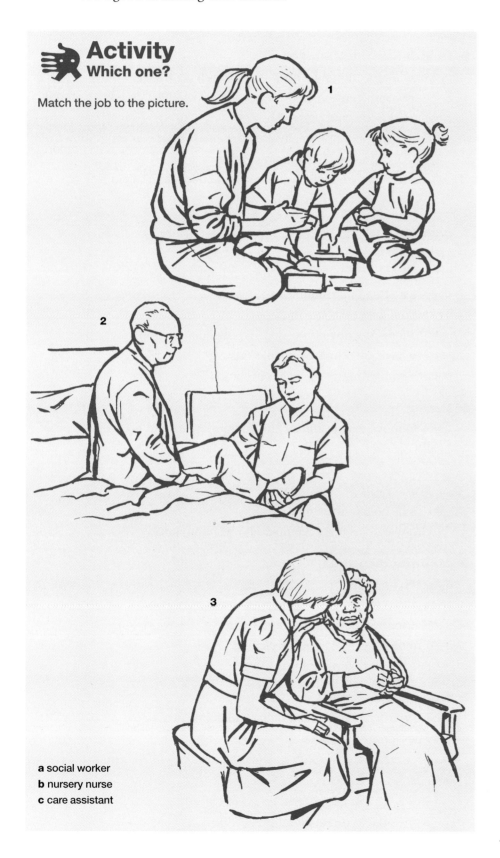

Activity
Which one?

Match the job to the picture.

1

2

3

a social worker

b nursery nurse

c care assistant

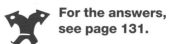

For the answers, see page 131.

Job roles in indirect care

Indirect care is provided by people who work 'behind the scenes' in a hospital or a health centre. They are an important part of the care team. They are sometimes in direct contact with clients. The include hospital porters, domestic assistants and doctors' receptionists. Indirect care is also provided by people who may not come into direct contact with patients, such as those who work in administration, management, catering and maintenance jobs.

The job roles include:

● **Health Service Manager**
  – responsible for running a hospital or health centre
  – organises and co-ordinates services such as medical, nursing, catering, cleaning services and porters
  Qualification – graduate management trainee scheme or promotion from role in NHS administration
  Need – to use analytical skills and be good at problem solving
        to have good interpersonal skills

● **Receptionist**
  – greets clients
  – arranges appointments for doctors and nurses
  – deals with telephone enquiries
  – carries out general office duties
  Qualification – not always needed. Typing qualification maybe useful
  Need – to have good interpersonal skills
        to communicate messages accurately

● **Porter**
  – helps to move clients, goods and equipment around the hospital or health centre
  – carries out a great deal of lifting and therefore needs to be physically fit.
  Qualification – no necessary qualification
  Need – to be able to use initiative
        to work as a team member and respond quickly

● **Maintenance staff**
  – keep the hospital, care home or health centre in good working order
  – responsible for general repairs and electrical work
  Qualification – needed in relevant areas, e.g. electrical work
  Need – to be good at practical tasks
        to be good at problem-solving

● **Domestic assistant**
  – cleans wards, toilets, bathrooms and kitchen areas
  – may work unusual hours
  – needs to communicate with staff and patients when performing their work
  Qualification – no necessary qualification
  Need – to work thoroughly and be conscientious
        to work as a team member

● Catering staff

– responsible for ordering and cooking food
– provide a choice of balanced menus
– cater for people with special diets
– work to a fixed time schedule and deliver meals on time

Qualification – may need NVQ in Catering

Need – to work to a time limit
to have good personal hygiene

● Administrator

– responsible for hospital records and appointment system
– appoints staff and deal with wages and salaries

Qualification – good general education including GCSE Mathematics and
GCSE English

Need – to have good, interpersonal skills
to be organised, accurate and pay attention to detail

● Clerical staff

– typing/word processing and office duties such as filing.

Qualification – may need GCSE's or NVQ in Business Administration

Need – to be accurate
to be able to work unsupervised

Activity
Jobs and skills

Make a table with these headings.

Nurse	Care assistant
1	1

Look at the ten job descriptions. Decide which job descriptions match which job titles (the first description has been done for you). Put them under the right headings – some will match both job titles.

1 I need good communication skills
2 I need patience, understanding, a caring attitude, reliability, calmness, honesty and to be able to get on with people
3 I need to be able to lift and handle clients safely
4 I look after clients in their own homes, care homes and day centres
5 I need job qualifications
6 I will need to be accurate when measuring and giving medication
7 I use practical skills like helping patients with toilet and hygiene needs, and feeding
8 I may need to be able to carry out domestic work and food preparation as well as laundry work
9 I will need to give verbal and written reports on a patient's condition and the treatment I have given
10 I need to be a good team member

For the answers,
see page 131.

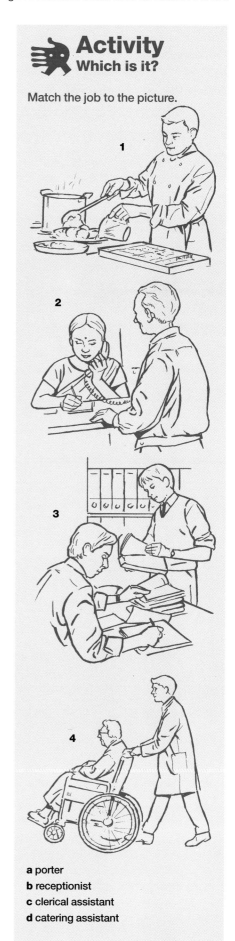

Activity
Which is it?

Match the job to the picture.

1
2
3
4

a porter
b receptionist
c clerical assistant
d catering assistant

For the answers,
see page 131.

Assignment
Mr and Mrs Underwood

Setting the scene
Read the case study and think carefully about all the people and the jobs involved in helping Mr and Mrs Underwood to live as independently as possible. You will use the information in the case study to produce a chart showing the different types of care supplied by the four health care providers.

Case study
Mr and Mrs Underwood

Mrs Underwood has cared for her husband, who had a stroke a number of years ago, which left him partially paralysed. They are both in their middle eighties. Mrs Underwood, who has osteoporosis, had to go into hospital recently to have an operation on her hip. Their doctor asked the social workers from the hospital and Social Services to help them to make decisions about Mr Underwood's care whilst his wife was in hospital and afterwards, whilst she got over her operation.

They decided that with the help of community health care assistants and the community/district nurse Mr Underwood would be able to remain at home. Mrs Underwood was admitted to hospital, was examined and X-rayed. Her operation was carried out successfully. She was cared for by the doctors and nurses in the hospital and received all the usual hospital services – meals, medicines, a clean and tidy ward with clean bedding. She listened to the hospital radio to help pass the time. She received flowers and cards from her friends and neighbours. She visited the hospital shop in a wheelchair when her visitors came. The physiotherapist visited her after the operation to help her to exercise and regain her mobility. The physiotherapist also prescribed outpatient care for Mrs Underwood on her return home.

When she left hospital Mrs Underwood was taken home by ambulance. After a few weeks, when she had fully recovered from the effects of the operation, she was left on her own to care for her husband. She found however that she could no longer continue to look after him properly. With the help and advice of the social worker, district/community nurse and the occupational therapist, the Underwoods moved into a specially adapted flat attached to a residential care home. They now live together independently in their flat with plenty of support on hand from the care workers and community care team. They are visited by the health visitor as well as the district nurse. The health visitor gives advice about lifestyle, for example diet, exercise and vaccinations. Mrs Underwood sees the physiotherapist when the physiotherapist visits her local day centre.

What does it mean?
- **Osteoporosis = a disease where bones become very thin and break easily.**

Task 1
Produce a care chart like the one below, with the headings shown. In the first column fill in who is providing the care: NHS, Social Services, private or voluntary sectors.

Task 2
In the second column write what type of care is being provided: health and medical care, community care and support, or indirect care.

Task 3
In the third column, put the job title of the person providing or organising the care. You will find at least two job roles for each type of care.

Task 4
In the last column write at least **two** purposes of the care provided by the people in each job role. The purposes might be:
- to diagnose injury or illness
- to provide medical or nursing care
- to provide remedial or therapeutic care
- to provide support
- to be educational.

Care chart

Provider of care	Type of care	Job title	Purpose of care
NHS	Health and medical care	Doctor	1 The doctor examines the patient (Mrs Underwood) and diagnoses the problem. 2 The doctor refers the patient to the hospital consultant

Opportunities to collect evidence
In this assignment you should cover:

Element 3.1
PCs 1, 2, 3, 4

For more on communication, see the Toolkit on pages 6 to 12.

Communication
Element 1.1, 1.2, 1.3, 1.4

?Quiz

How much do you know about working in health and social care?

 See page 155 for the answers.

Each question shows more than one possible answer, **a**, **b**, **c** and **d**; only one is correct.

1 The NHS provides:
  a free treatment from doctors and nurses
  b free treatment for children and elderly people only
  c a few free health services
  d free dental care for all ages

2 Private health care means that:
  a you have to pay for your own medical/nursing care
  b the state pays for your care
  c you have chosen to pay for your own medical/nursing care
  d the care is paid for by your employers.

3 Voluntary care services are paid for by:
  a the people receiving care
  b society as a whole by charity donations
  c society and the government
  d a mixture of **a**, **b** and **c**

4 Home care assistants *usually* work for:
  a Age Concern
  b Social Services
  c NHS
  d voluntary day care centres

5 A physiotherapist gives:
  a health and medical care
  b care and support
  c respite care
  d indirect care

6 A doctor's receptionist gives:
  a indirect care
  b health and medical care
  c care and support
  d day care

7 An X-ray is taken by:
  a radiographer
  b physiotherapist
  c X-ray support staff
  d occupational therapist

8 A health visitor's duties include:
  a delivering babies
  b changing dressings
  c visiting mothers with infants and children under school age
  d prescribing medicines

Scoring

If you got:
● between 1 and 4 – you need to develop your knowledge of the job roles in health and social care. Ask your tutor for advice.
● between 5 and 7 – you have a reasonable understanding of the job roles. What weren't you sure about?
● 8 and above – you have a very good understanding of this element.

Answers

p.125 Activity – Match them up
1 – g, 2 – a, 3 – b, 4 – e, 5 – c, 6 – f, 7 – d

p.127 Activity – Which one?
1 – b, 2 – c, 3 – a

p.129 Activity – Jobs and skills

Nurse	Care assistant
1 2 3 5 6 9 10	1 2 3 4 7 8 10

p.129 Activity – Which is it?
1 – d, 2 – b, 3 – c, 4 -a

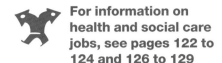

For information on health and social care jobs, see pages 122 to 124 and 126 to 129

Investigate jobs in health and social care

In this element you will look at jobs in health and social care and discover whether they are likely to suit you. You will be thinking about jobs you can do when you leave school or college, and jobs that you could move on to.

By the end of this element you should be able to:

- identify two jobs in health and social care which are likely to suit you
- describe the main purposes of each identified job
- explain why each identified job is likely to suit you
- identify the main skills required for each identified job
- identify the qualifications required for each identified job
- identify how to obtain the skills and qualifications required for each identified job
- seek advice and information from appropriate sources.

Career progression

Few jobs in health and social care have very large salaries, but some jobs offer a reasonable salary to start with and offer good **career progression,** and salaries increase according to age and experience. The job of a health care assistant taking NVQ (National Vocational Qualification) Levels 2 and 3 does not attract a large salary but does offer you a chance to improve your knowledge and skills. You can then move on into other areas of health care if you wish.

What shall I do when I leave school or college?

People often have difficulty deciding which job or career to choose. One reason is that there are so many types of job available. Another reason is that they may not have thought about their abilities and interests and matched them to a job. You need to not only think about a first job, but look further ahead to jobs which offer you progression, for example health and social care sector jobs.

When you start looking for a job you may find that at first there is only part-time work available in your chosen area. Taking a part-time job gives you the opportunity to show employers that you are reliable and trustworthy and can cope with the work involved. Part-time employment usually gives you a good start when a full-time job becomes available, and your employer will be able to give you a **reference**.

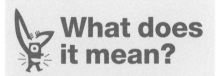

What does it mean?

- **Career progression = being promoted to a higher position until you reach the top.**

What does it mean?

- **Reference = a letter describing your character, quality and abilities.**

Suitable jobs for suitable people

When you start thinking about what you want to do when you leave school or college for your **initial employment**, you need to do the following.

- Decide what your strengths and weaknesses are. Think about your skills and qualifications and match all these with the job you would like to do. This will help you to decide whether a particular job will suit you or not.

- Find out as much as possible about the available job opportunities locally. The available opportunities for a job in health and social care, or in any other career, will vary from one locality to another. In your neighbourhood there may not be a hospital for example. If you decide you want a career related to hospital work then you may have to relocate (move) unless you are prepared to travel further to work.

- Think about what the availability of jobs will be in the future. You could ask for careers advice to see what jobs should be available to you when you have finished studying. This may be in a few years time.

- Try and get first-hand experience by work placement, a part-time job or by speaking to people in jobs in areas that you think may interest you. This will help you to see what they are really like.

- Find out the tasks that are carried out in particular jobs that interest you and what responsibilities the jobs carry. You can research this and make notes of your findings.

- Find out how to obtain further qualifications and skills, if you need them for the job or jobs that interest you now or in the future.

You also need to consider what your initial employment might progress on to. In this way you are thinking about your longer-term career.

 For more on carrying out research, see the Toolkit on pages 3 and 4.

What do they mean?

- **Initial employment = Your first job.**

Jobs available
Sewing machinist
Secretary
Car mechanic
Care assistant

Are they suitable?
Can I type?
Can I sew?
Will it be a good career?
Am I good at fixing things?

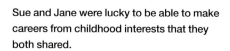
Sue and Jane were lucky to be able to make careers from childhood interests that they both shared.

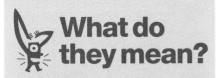

What do they mean?

- **Circumstances = Situation,** for example where you live, the hours you can work.

- **Skill = A special ability in a task or situation.**

- **Vocational = related to a particular job or career.**

- **Core skills = Key skills** including communication, IT and application of number

- **Academic = Able to study the theory of a subject and do coursework and exams**

- **Temperament = How you react to others, for example, whether you are calm, energetic, cheerful or quiet.**

Suiting you

If you are very fortunate, both your interests and qualifications may match a job exactly, for example, fashion designer, artist, musician, footballer. For most of us this is not possible. You need to consider what is available that suits your **circumstances** and interests as well as considering what **skills** and qualifications are needed. Remember skills include both **vocational** and **core skills**. Qualifications can include both **academic** (e.g. GCSEs) and vocational qualifications (GNVQS and NVQS). You should also aim to find a job that you think you will enjoy as it suits your personality and **temperament**.

You probably have not thought much about yourself in this way before. If you want to have a career in caring you will eventually be responsible for the care of other people. You will need to learn about their likes and dislikes and understand why they behave as they do when they are being cared for. To understand other people, you need to learn about yourself first.

Understanding yourself

Activity
How do others see me?

Ask your parents, family and friends to describe what you are like as a person. Write down all the words that people use about you. They might use words like these:

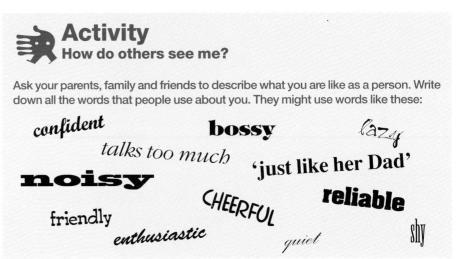

At interviews you will be asked about yourself, and sometimes asked to write a personal statement about yourself. You need to develop an understanding of yourself to help you do this.

Activity
This is me

Look at the headings and comments surrounding this person and think about how they apply to you. Make a copy of this page and underneath each heading note down what applies to you, e.g. list a few of your hobbies. Do not worry if you are a bit unsure, one of the purposes of the activity is to learn more about yourself and your suitability for a career in caring.

This is me

Academic
Are you 'brainy' or average? Write about the academic examinations (e.g. GCSEs) you have undertaken and your results.

Vocational
What experience and knowledge have you got about the world of work? What work experience have you done? Have you got or had a part-time job?

Temperament
Are you even tempered and calm or quick tempered, thoughtful, 'laid back'? Do you cope well under pressure?

Personality
What sort of personality do you have? Lively or quiet, outgoing or shy? Do you find it hard to deal with people in authority and outside your own family and friends?

Hobbies
Do you collect things or make things, for example CD collecting, computing, sewing, painting?

Appearance
Are you tidy or scruffy, fit and healthy-looking or pale and unfit?

Qualities
Are you caring, well motivated, enthusiastic, trustworthy?

Interests
What are they? Dancing, watching television, talking to friends? Are you in any clubs, societies or groups?

Skills
Think about the core skills you are developing on your GNVQ course.
Are you good at solving problems, or organising yourself and other people? Is your time-keeping good? Are you good at managing your own money? Are you good at talking to people? Are you a good team member? Have you any practical skills such as sewing, painting, DIY, model making?

Foundation GNVQ Health & Social Care © Hadfield, Towers and Wray, 1996.
Published by Thomas Nelson & Sons Ltd.

 **For more on the qualities needed for work as a carer, see page 137.**

Activity
My qualities

Look at this list and try to decide which qualities you possess and write them down. Sometimes people find this difficult to do, so you could ask your parents or someone else who knows you well to help you. Your personal qualities are the good things about you. They are part of your personality and make you the person you are. For example, someone may have caring qualities, but lack a sense of humour.

responsible
caring
approachable
well-motivated
respectful
good at solving problems
reliable
trustworthy
good communicator
practical
kind
hard working
good team member
honest
confident
enthusiastic
able to use initiative
courteous
committed
sense of humour

Developing your self awareness

Developing your understanding of yourself (your self-awareness) means being aware of your weak areas as well as your strengths. The activity **This is me** asked you to look at yourself more carefully than usual. You will have thought about your abilities in different areas. For instance, you may have many skills. Some may be good 'people' skills, that is, talking and getting on with other people. Some people are good at academic things like mathematics or a language. Remember, it is valuable to know your weaker areas are so that you can work towards improving them.

There are many qualities that make a good carer. When you apply for jobs that involve caring, you may be asked what your qualities are.

In caring jobs it is important to have the right blend of qualities, abilities and skills.

Activity
Improved caring

Look at **A**, **B** and **C**. As a group, brainstorm how the attitude of these carers could be improved.

Qualities needed in a caring job

Caring jobs need people who are reliable, have stamina and, above all, are caring. A carer needs to be good at working as a team member and coping with work under pressure. Job applicants need to have good practical skills and a sound knowledge of everything to do with the caring process. In any job connected with health and social care you will need good communication skills, the ability to adapt and use initiative. If you are inexperienced, you need to show that you have the enthusiasm and commitment to learn.

For more on job roles and qualifications see pages 122 to 124 and 126 to 129.

Suitable jobs

If you think that you have the right skills, qualifications and qualities to be a carer then you need to find a suitable job.

Some people find that they are very good at the practical side of caring, but do not want to do a great deal of studying or undertake the coursework and exams involved. They may find, for example, that being a health care assistant or health support worker in physiotherapy is the right option for them, rather than being a nurse or a physiotherapist.

Where to get help advice and information

Whatever kind of work you decide is suitable for you, you need to get as much advice as possible from appropriate sources before you decide. There are plenty of people in many different places to ask. Your local Careers and

Guidance Advisers will be able to give you sound advice and answer your queries. You could check with your tutor whether they think you are suitable for a job in caring. You could ask health and social care workers how they got started in their careers, whether they have academic qualifications, or vocational qualifications such as NVQs. Ask them if they intend to gain any more qualifications. Work experience is a good opportunity to find out more about careers in caring.

There are many career reference materials to use these days. Not only books and leaflets, but CD-ROMS and computer programmes including the *Careers Information Database (CID)* and *Kudos* (an interactive package).

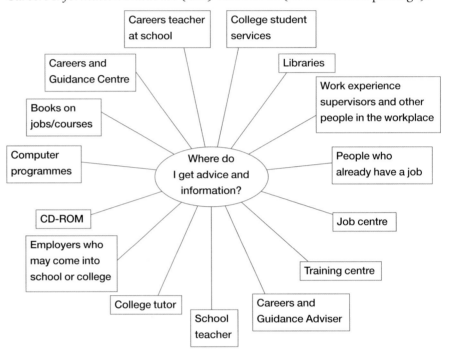

Training for care work

If you go to work anywhere in Europe at the age of 16, 17 or 18 and you do not have any NVQs you may be asked if you are willing to take up training and supervised learning, perhaps with day release to college, to help you achieve an NVQ whilst you are doing the job. If you go on a Youth Training scheme you will be working towards an NVQ.

You can begin at NVQ Level 1 and progress to NVQ Level 5 which is equivalent to degree level study. NVQs are an alternative to the academic route to qualifications and are accepted for many jobs. For example, it is likely that you will be accepted for nursing training with NVQ Level 3 in care. For some jobs, however, such as a physiotherapist, you would probably need an academic qualification as well as NVQs.

Ways to gain qualifications

There are different ways to gain the qualifications for jobs that you might choose to do later in your health and social care career – the picture shows some of the wide range of possibilities. The qualifications needed can vary from area to area, and they do change with time. You always need to check details when you are thinking about a particular pathway.

Social work training leading to Registered Social Worker 2 or 3 years

Work experience <u>plus</u> A levels – 2 years +

Work experience <u>plus</u> Foundation Health & Social Care GNVQ <u>plus</u> Intermediate Health & Social Care GNVQ <u>plus</u> Advanced Health & Social Care GNVQ – 4 years

GNVQ Advanced Health & Social Care – 2 years <u>plus</u> work experience

Open College credits plus experience

Mature student with work experience and evidence of recent study. e.g. ACCESS/A Levels

Qualified Nursery Nurse
BTEC National Diploma in Nursery Nursing – 2 years
NNEB Diploma in Nursery Nursing – 2 years

GNVQ Intermediate with good grades

Nursery support worker <u>plus</u> evidence of academic ability and commitment

NVQ Level 2 in Child Care and good portfolio

GCSEs in C/D range plus experience with children

Qualified Health Care Assistant leading to Senior Health Care Assistant <u>plus</u> least 2 years' work experience

GNVQ Foundation Health & Social Care <u>plus</u> Work experience <u>plus</u> NVQ Level 2

Youth Training <u>plus</u> NVQ Health & Social Care Level 2

Job as Health Care Assistant (no qualifications) <u>plus</u> NVQ Level 2 part-time <u>plus</u> College 1 day/week

Nurse training – 3/4 years
Project 2000 or BA Nursing

5 GCSEs

A levels – 2 years

GCSEs 1 year <u>plus</u> A levels – 2 years

Foundation GNVQ in Health and Social Care – 1 year; Intermediate -1 year; Advanced – 2 years

BTEC Health Studies – 2 years

Intermediate GNVQ 1 year; Advanced – 2 years

Health Care Assistant NVQ Level 2 – 1/2 years <u>plus</u> NVQ Level 3 – 2 years

NVQ Level 3 – 2 years

Open College Stage B Certificates

Occupational Therapist – 3 years

Health Support Worker in Occupational Therapy <u>plus</u> NVQ Level 2 <u>plus</u> Further Education qualifications

GCSEs and A levels

Physiotherapy Training leading to Qualified Physiotherapist – 3/4 years

Health Support Worker in Physiotherapy <u>plus</u> NVQ Level 2 <u>plus</u> Further Education qualifications

GCSEs and A levels

Occupational therapy · **Health care** · **Social work** · **Child care** · **Nursing** · **Physiotherapy**

Which pathway?

Which pathway?

Activity
Two suitable jobs

Uzma is 16 and is leaving school in the summer. She is not very academic but likes practical work and solving problems in a work situation. She has a Saturday job in a care home where her sister works as a Senior Health Care Assistant. Uzma enjoys chatting to the elderly residents. She plays bingo and dominoes with them, as well as doing kitchen duties and general helping. She is not sure what she wants to do in the future, but would like to get some qualifications.

Look at the five advertisements and say which jobs would be suitable for Uzma now and which might be suitable later in her career. Give reasons for your answers.

You could look back at job roles to help you, see pages 122 to 124 and 126 to 129.

Peter has gained his Foundation Health & Social Care GNVQ at college and is looking for a job that involves caring for people, but he does not want to go into health care. He would rather help people to sort out their problems, perhaps when they are homeless or have to be cared for on a full-time basis. Peter does not have many qualifications yet but he is willing to go to his local college on a part-time basis now, or on a full-time basis later, to gain more qualifications.

Look at the advertisements again and decide which would be the most suitable jobs for Peter now and in the future.

Hall Park Nursing Home Care Assistant

Applicant needs to be 17+ with some experience of care and be willing to undertake NVQ Level 2 training. Please apply in writing to the matron.

42 The Meadows
Sunnybridge
Surrey
KT2 4HL

Lincolnshire Disability and Mental Health Service

Mental Health Worker

Would you like to be part of an innovative care team? We need an enthusiastic person to join our team. You will need

- a relevant professional qualification
- group work experience
- excellent communication skills
- knowledge of community health care legislation
- an enthusiastic and creative approach.

Job ref 1270/3

Smithfield Healthcare Trust

Ward Sister

To run this busy 16 bedded surgical unit you need

- 3 years post registration experience
- the ability to run a care team
- to be able to supervise Project 2000 learners
- to be able to manage the introduction of IT to ward situation
- to be able to manage resources and budgets.

Ring Human Resources Manager
Tel: 01242 65182

Senior Care Assistant

Required for Garthdale Home for the Elderly, Wolstencroft, Derby

Must have Level 2 NVQ in Care and 3 years experience in caring.

Must be able to work well in a team and supervise junior care and cleaning staff.

Please apply in writing to Mrs Barret

The Winnows

Residential Care Home
4 Bell Close
Street, Somerset

Youth Training Vacancy

Applicants must have good interpersonal skills, be clean and tidy looking and be willing to use initiative. Must be enthusiastic about working in caring.

Apply in writing to: Mr H Clough.

 Assignment

Which job first?

Setting the scene

Imagine that you have completed your Foundation Health & Social Care GNVQ and you are working in your first job. Your friend Pat asks for your advice on working in health and social care. You tell Pat all about your first job, and about the job you intend to move on to.

Task 1

Think about all that you have learnt about yourself – abilities, skills and personality – and the information you have gathered from the previous element, together with any information from other sources. Decide what your first job might have been and what job you might want to move on to.

Task 2

Describe the main purpose of the first job and the job you intend to move on to.

Task 3

List the qualifications you needed for your first job and the job you want to move on to.

Task 4

Give Pat written advice on the different ways in which he/she can get qualifications, for example, part-time study whilst in a job, or the different pathways for full-time study.

Task 5

Explain to someone in your group why you decided to do one of the jobs described in Task 2. Explain/describe your

● qualities

● skills

and why you think the job suits you. Keep a record of these for your portfolio.

Task 6

List sources of information and advice: the books, leaflets and people that might help.

 For information on job roles, skills and pathways, see pages 122 to 124 and 126 to 129.

Opportunities to collect evidence

In this assignment you should cover:

Element 3.2
PCs 1, 2, 3, 4, 5, 6, 7

Communication
Element 1.1, 1.2, 1.4

?Quiz

How much do you know about investigating jobs?

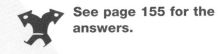

See page 155 for the answers.

Each question shows more than one possible answer, **a**, **b**, **c** and **d**; only one is correct.

1 Which of these four jobs would be suitable for a 16 year old school leaver wishing to find a **first** job in health care?
   a practice nurse
   b youth trainee taking NVQ level 2 Direct Care
   c residential social worker
   d Senior Care Assistant

2 Which of the following might your Careers and Guidance Adviser have information on?
   a 18–30 foreign holidays
   b income tax forms
   c general information on jobs and employment
   d national insurance

3 Vocational qualifications mean:
   a only GNVQs
   b only NVQs
   c GNVQs and NVQs
   d A levels

4 Which one of the following jobs would be suitable for someone who is 22 years old with four years experience as a care assistant and NVQ level 2 Care?
   a Senior Care Assistant in a residential home
   b Senior Social Worker
   c Matron of a nursing home
   d Officer in Charge of a social services residential home

5 Which of the following would be an essential skill for someone to work as a carer?
   a English as a first language
   b ability to work alone
   c good at sewing and knitting
   d good communication skills

6 Where would be the *best* place to look for a job vacancy in your local area?
   a a book on careers
   b *Yellow Pages*
   c the local newspaper
   d national television

7 Where would you get information about *your* suitability for a job in caring?
   a dictionary
   b school report
   c application form
   d careers and guidance adviser or careers library

8 Which would be a suitable course for someone with Foundation GNVQ to gain a further qualification in Health and Social Care?
   a NVQ Level 3 in care
   b Advanced GNVQ Health & Social Care
   c A level in psychology
   d Intermediate GNVQ Health & Social Care

Scoring

If you got:

● between 1 and 3 – you need to brush up on your knowledge and ask advice.

● between 4 and 6 – your understanding of this element is reasonable. Check that you understand the work you have covered.

● 7 and above – your understanding of where to find help and advice for a suitable job for yourself is very good.

Plan for employment in health and social care

This element gives you information to help you get a job. You need to know where to find jobs and how to apply for them so that you give yourself the best chance of being chosen.

By the end of this element you should be able to:

- identify personal information and produce a curriculum vitae (CV)
- describe the main ways to find out about job vacancies in health and social care
- describe the main stages in recruitment in health and social care
- describe different ways of presenting personal information to **prospective** employers
- seek advice and information from appropriate sources.

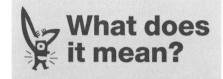

What does it mean?

- **Prospective = future.**

What does it mean?

- **Mock interview** = when someone pretends to be an employer and asks you similar questions to those you will have in a real interview.

- **Initiative** = able to do things without being told by others.

Where do I get advice and information?

Careers and Guidance Centre

You may have had an interview with your Careers and Guidance Adviser from the local careers office. If not, you can call in or telephone – details of your nearest office are in the telephone directory. Careers staff in schools and colleges can also give advice and information.

Careers and Guidance Advisers are professional advisers who are specially trained and can:

- help you to assess your skills, strengths and weaknesses
- carry out **mock interviews**
- take part in careers conventions
- give information and advice on job training schemes and further and higher education courses to help you to gain additional qualifications for a job
- give information on jobs and what is on offer in the local job market. They visit employers to keep up-to-date.

Job Centre

Jobs advertised here are usually for people with some experience. However, it can be useful to have a look inside. There are staff are available to help you or you can just look at the noticeboard inside.

Employment agencies

These agencies usually have details of office and factory jobs, but some specialise in particular areas such as care, nursing or nannies. Care agencies are usually for qualified staff. Once you have some experience they are worth trying.

Where do I look?

Media

Look in newspapers – local weekly and evening papers, job magazines, 'free' newspapers, for the job section where jobs are advertised.

Local shops

Jobs are advertised in corner shops, supermarkets and chain stores.

Yourself

Some jobs are never advertised so you need to think about approaching employers directly. This means telephoning, visiting or writing to an establishment and asking if they have any vacancies. This shows that you are using your **initiative**. If they do not have a job, ask if they will put your name on a waiting list and let you know if a job becomes available. Do not be afraid to go back again at a later date.

Friends and relatives

Friends and relatives may know of vacancies and be able to recommend you. Let people help you to get started in your career.

Aunty Sue told me about a vacancy for a care assistant at the home where she works

 For more on where to get advice and information see pages 137 to 138.

The main stages in job recruitment

Employers go through five stages when they are **recruiting** people. **Applicants** may go through all the stages if they are successful, but only some if they are unsuccessful. Some stages are more involved than others. For example, applying for a job means a lot of hard work for the applicant but little work for the employer. Selecting and interviewing job applicants take up more of the employer's time.

Five point plan of recruitment

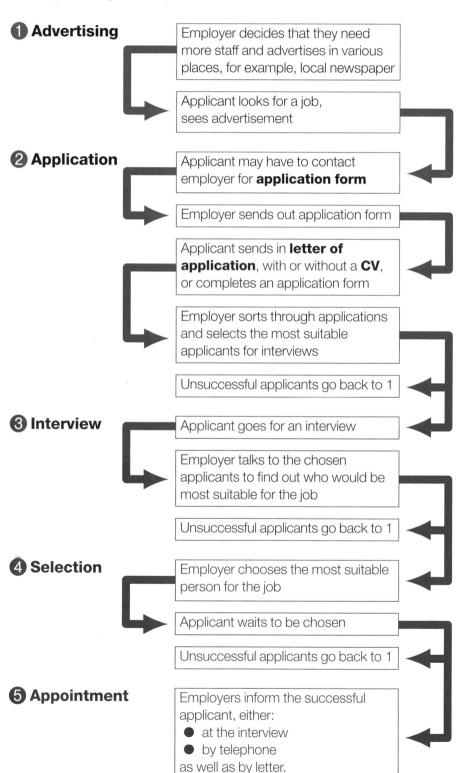

❶ **Advertising**

> Employer decides that they need more staff and advertises in various places, for example, local newspaper

> Applicant looks for a job, sees advertisement

❷ **Application**

> Applicant may have to contact employer for **application form**

> Employer sends out application form

> Applicant sends in **letter of application**, with or without a **CV**, or completes an application form

> Employer sorts through applications and selects the most suitable applicants for interviews

> Unsuccessful applicants go back to 1

❸ **Interview**

> Applicant goes for an interview

> Employer talks to the chosen applicants to find out who would be most suitable for the job

> Unsuccessful applicants go back to 1

❹ **Selection**

> Employer chooses the most suitable person for the job

> Applicant waits to be chosen

> Unsuccessful applicants go back to 1

❺ **Appointment**

> Employers inform the successful applicant, either:
> - at the interview
> - by telephone
> as well as by letter.

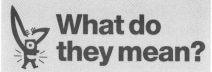

What do they mean?

- **Recruitment** = the process of finding the right person for a particular job.
- **Applicant** = person applying for a particular job.

> We need more staff!

What does it mean?

- **Application form** = form which requests personal details, such as skills, previous experience and qualities.

> Tell us about yourself.

What do they mean?

- **Letter of application** = a letter containing personal details, such as previous experience skills, and qualities. Employers prefer it to be handwritten.

- **CV** = a record or list of what you have done with your life so far. It gives employers your personal details and lists your achievements.

Applicants may have to sign and return a **contract of employment**. You must get advice before signing this, perhaps from your family, someone who has worked in care or the **Citizens Advice Bureau.** Check the details with your new employer if you are unsure.

What do they mean?

- **Contract of employment =** a written agreement signed by you and the employer giving details of the terms and conditions for the job, such as hours of work, and holidays.

- **Citizens Advice Bureau =** a free service offering advice. Look in your telephone directory for your local office.

Before applying for a job

Before you apply for a job that you think might interest you, look very carefully at the advertisement. Ask yourself these kind of questions about it.

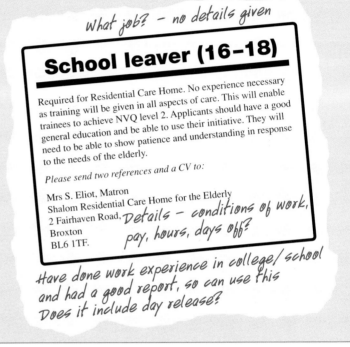

What job? – no details given

School leaver (16–18)

Required for Residential Care Home. No experience necessary as training will be given in all aspects of care. This will enable trainees to achieve NVQ level 2. Applicants should have a good general education and be able to use their initiative. They will need to be able to show patience and understanding in response to the needs of the elderly.

Please send two references and a CV to:

Mrs S. Eliot, Matron
Shalom Residential Care Home for the Elderly
2 Fairhaven Road,
Broxton
BL6 1TF.

Details – conditions of work, pay, hours, days off?

Have done work experience in college/school and had a good report, so can use this
Does it include day release?

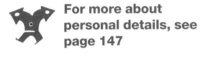

For more about personal details, see page 147

Ways of presenting personal information

When you apply for a job you need to be sure that you are sending in the right **personal details**, so check the advertisement and see what you need to do. If you need to fill in an application form, contact the employer and ask them to send you one or call in for one. Some employers ask for a letter of application and possibly a CV as well.

Letters of application, application forms and CVs are all different ways of presenting personal information. This is a very important stage. Applying for the job and the interview are the hardest parts – these are the stages where you have to 'sell yourself' and convince the employer that you are the best person for the job.

Personal information includes:
- subjects studied
- qualifications/awards
- personal qualities
- experience and achievements gained through work and training
- any other achievements
- leisure activities (sports and hobbies for example)

Remember to include current and previous achievement both inside and outside school or college. Include membership of groups and clubs.

Your CV (curriculum vitae)

A CV needs to include the following personal information:

Personal details – name, address, telephone number, age

Education – details of your college or school and course(s) you are studying, for example, GCSEs, Foundation GNVQs, NVQs, City & Guilds, RSA, BTEC

Qualifications – the subjects you have already gained at GCSE, GNVQ, NVQ, City & Guilds and so on

Work experience – any employment you have had, including part-time holiday work and work experience

Interests – any hobbies, sports or group activities or voluntary work, such as baby-sitting, or shopping for an elderly person, which you think might show what type of person you are. Don't list too many!

Additional information – any skills or information that you have not been able to include elsewhere; for example, you may have computer skills, be a good team member, be good at communicating or be learning to drive. Include other qualifications, such as a first aid certificate. You could also add your qualities, for example, you are trustworthy, honest and have a good sense of humour.

Referees – the names, addresses and positions (for example, tutor, employer, headteacher, Scout leader) of two people who know you well. Always remember to ask if you can use their names.

For information on finding out about your qualities, see page 136.

CURRICULUM VITAE

NAME: Sally Myles

ADDRESS: 2 Bedington Road,
Christchurch,
Borwick,
B52 4EO

DATE OF BIRTH: 14.5.78

EDUCATION:
1995-present: Collybourne College, Borwick
1991 – 1995 Culdee School, Borwick

QUALIFICATIONS AWAITED:
At the moment I am studying for my GNVQ certificate in Health & Social Care. I am trying to improve my communication, numeracy and IT skills, which are also part of my course.

ACHIEVED:
GCSEs: English Language: F; Child Care: D; Science: E; Maths U

WORK EXPERIENCE:
I have completed two work experience placements, each for two weeks:
1995 September – Little Rascals Nursery – general work
1996 June – Sunnyfield Care Home for the Elderly – care assistant

INTERESTS:
I like listening to music and socialising with my friends.
I enjoy doing aerobics.

ADDITIONAL INFORMATION:
I run errands at the weekend for my grandmother and her neighbours. I have a first aid certificate.

REFERENCES:
Mr C. Duncan,
Culdee School,
Borwick.
B52 4TL.

Mrs C. Ratcliffe,
Sunnyfield Care Home for the Elderly,
Brunshaw Road,
Borwick.
B9 2TL.

Activity
Write your own CV

Write your own CV. Word process it if you can.

What does it mean?

- **National Record of Achievement = booklet or document showing school or college achievements, attendance, skills and work experience details. You should take this to job interviews.**

When putting together your CV remember to:

- keep the information to the point – you will have a chance to give more detailed information about yourself at the interview
- put the information on your latest experiences and qualifications first
- use only one side of the paper – you do not have to write in sentences
- word process it if you can – it is easier to update if you keep it on disk and it is easier to fit in all the information
- set it out well so that it is easy to read.

National Record of Achievement

You may be putting your own CV together with the help of your teacher or college tutor as part of your **National Record of Achievement**.

How do I write a letter of application?

Letter writing may be an important part of applying for a job. If you are asked to write a letter of application:

- check the advertisement to make sure that you include all the relevant details about yourself
- include the name of the job that you are applying for
- say why you are interested in this particular job
- say why you will be suitable for the job – qualifications, skills and qualities
- write in paragraphs and keep the information short
- handwrite the letter if possible
- check for correct spelling and punctuation.

Activity
Job application

This activity will help you to write a letter of application for a job for which you wish to apply.

Look carefully at the job advertisement for the Mental Health Worker on page 140, then using the table:

- make a list of the skills and qualities stated and any other you think will be needed to do the job (look through this unit for ideas)
- match each skill/quality to any experience you have.

Some examples have been filled in.

Skill/quality	Experience
patience	baby sitting for children aged 18 months – 3 years
understanding the needs of elderly people	work experience
good at communicating	

Activity
Application analysis

Look at this letter of application and the accompanying job advertisement.

> 11 Parkgate
> Blackwell
>
> Matron
> Sunnyview Rest Home
> Blackwell
> BB10 4TL
>
> Dear Sir
>
> I would like to apply for the job that I saw IN THE job centre.
> I am 16 years of age and hope to complete my collage course in June.
> I am also hoping to improve my grades in GCSE English.
>
> The course I am studying includes learning about care of the elderly.
> I think that I will make a good care assistant. I am trustworthy and
> reliable and people tell me that I have a lot of pacience with my
> elderly grandparents. I enjoyed my work experience at school
> and college.
>
> My scholl form teacher and college tutor have offered to give
> me refrences.
>
> I enjoy listening to music and socialising with my friends. My other
> interest is swimming and I have recently started aerobic classes.
> I will be available anytime for interview.
>
> Yours sincerly
>
> Jayna Begum

Sunnyview Rest Home

We are looking for an enthusiastic school / college leaver to work as a Care Assistant. Experience preferable but not essential. Training will be provided.

For details apply to:

Mrs Kathryn Sanderson
Matron
Sunnyview Rest Home
Blackwell
BB10 4TL

1 Under two headings, list:
- the good points and
- the bad points
  of the letter.
2 Write any other comments.
3 Rewrite the letter in a way that would improve it and would make sure that an employer did not throw it into the waste bin.

Activity
Letter of application

Find advertisements in local papers for jobs you could apply for when you leave school or college. Stick these onto a sheet of A4 paper. If you are unable to find anything suitable, apply for the Youth Training job on page 140. Write a letter of application for one job, saying which one it is. Do it in rough first and ask your teacher or tutor to check it before doing a final copy. Don't forget that you are trying to 'sell yourself', so put in previous experience, skills and all the qualities that will help you to get the job.

 For information on writing a formal letter, see the Toolkit on page 10.

For a blank application form that you can photocopy and practise filling in, see the Toolkit on page 30.

Activity
Using application forms

As a group, collect a range of application forms from local care establishments or from other local employers and the Careers and Guidance Adviser – they often hold forms for training schemes. You could write, telephone or call in for your forms. When you have collected your forms, compare them to see if the same types of care establishments ask for the same type of information. Then use one form to fill in your own details.

How do I fill in application forms?

The important word is – *carefully*!

Employers use application forms as a way of making sure that they have all the information they need. They are also able to file them easily. They usually contain all the information that is contained in a CV or letter of application, but they do not have as much space, so you may need to make your handwriting smaller.

When filling in an application form:
- read the whole form carefully before you start
- check any information that you do not understand
- keep your handwriting small and neat
- use a black pen
- fill in the form in pencil first or photocopy the form and use the photocopy as a practice form.

When you have completed the form:
- check to make sure that you have answered all the sections correctly
- check your spelling and punctuation
- ask someone to check it through for you
- keep a photocopy of the completed form.

Checkpoints for letter, CV and application form
- **always** check that your information is correct
- **always** check spellings and punctuation
- **always** make sure that your application is well presented
- **always** ask someone to check it for you. Many applications are rejected on first reading because of simple spelling mistakes, poor presentation and because the information they present is not what the employer asked for in the advertisement.
- try to word process your CV – keeping it on disk means that it's easier to change

How do I find out what to do at the interview?

Look at these guidelines. Also ask for advice from teachers, tutors, Careers and Guidance Advisers, and parents and friends who have had interviews. You may be able to have practice interviews at college, school or with the careers adviser. Get as much information and practice as possible.

Interview guidelines

DO ✔

- ☐ check appearance
- ☐ check personal freshness and cleanliness
- ☐ have neat and tidy clothes
- ☐ check how long it will take to get there
- ☐ try to visit the place the day before if you are not sure where to go
- ☐ check that you have any necessary documents – your Record of Achievement, copy of your CV, copy of the application form
- ☐ write any questions on a piece of paper, keep it handy and ask if you can refer to it if you need to
- ☐ have an explanation ready for why you want employment in a caring situation
- ☐ have some questions of your own ready. Employers will expect you to ask about conditions of work – holidays, uniform and what the job requires for example
- ☐ look interested, use eye contact, smile and try to relax (not an easy thing to do)
- ☐ ask for an explanation of things that you are not clear about
- ☐ think about your **body language**
- ☐ ask the interviewer to repeat a question if you have not understood it.

DON'T ✘

- ☐ wear jeans or trainers
- ☐ wear lots of jewellery or outrageous hairstyles
- ☐ be late – try to be at least 10 minutes early
- ☐ say 'I need a job' or 'What's the pay like?' or just say that you like working with people
- ☐ sit down unless you're asked to or cross your legs or look bored
- ☐ try to answer a question if you do not know the answer – be prepared to say 'I'm sorry, I don't know.'
- ☐ speak too quickly (even though it is difficult when you're nervous).

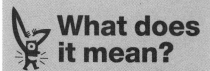

What does it mean?

- ● Body language = a way of showing thoughts and feelings by the way you move or position your face and body.

For more on body language, see the Toolkit on page 9.

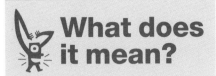

What does it mean?

● **Interviewee = person being interviewed.**

Activity
Job advertisements

Work in a group of four or less. Form an interview team of not more than three people. Using job advertisements from the local paper or the advertisement for a care assistant at Sunnyview Rest Home on page 149, draw up a checklist of suitable questions and 'interview' the other member of your group. Think about body language and dress and how well your **interviewee** answers the questions. Have one turn each at being the interviewee.

Assignment
The careers exhibition

Setting the scene

Your local Careers and Guidance Centre plans to hold a mini-careers exhibition, aimed at informing students about job opportunities in the area and what they need to do to get a job.

The careers advisers have asked Foundation groups including Foundation GNVQ Health & Social Care students to help stage the exhibition. You are to provide information about how to plan for a job in health and social care.

Task 1

Make a display (A3-sized or larger) which shows the different ways to find out about job vacancies in your area. Include a collection of different vacancies from newspaper advertisements, the Job Centre, shop noticeboards and so on. Record the display on video or take photographs of it as part of your evidence.

Task 2

Use one of the vacancies which appeals to you as the basis for writing, word processing and printing out a simple CV and letter of application using your own details.

Use the CV and letter as examples for the exhibition – mount them as part of the display, or make them into a factsheet. Include hints on how to complete both a CV and a letter of application. You could record this on video or take photographs of it.

Task 3

Produce a simple guide to completing application forms. Include a completed copy of an application form, using your own details, as an example. There is one for you to photocopy in the Toolkit (see page 30.)

Task 4

Arrange to interview the manager of a residential care or nursing home. This can be done individually or as a group. Ask them what stages they go through when they want to appoint someone to a vacancy. Produce a chart which shows the information as clearly and simply as possible and use this to feed back to your tutor.

Produce a chart which shows this information as clearly and simply as possible.

Task 5

Make a list of the most useful people to contact when seeking help about jobs, and describe the types of information and advice they might give. Use this as part of your display. You could interview at least one of these people and record their advice.

Opportunities to collect evidence

In this assignment you should cover:

Element 3.3
  PCs 1, 2, 3, 4, 5
Information Technology
  Element 1.2, 1.2, 1.3

Communication
  Element 1.1, 1.2, 1.3

?Quiz

Check your knowledge of planning for employment

See page 155 for the answers.

Each question shows more than one possible answer, **a**, **b**, **c** and **d**; only one is correct.

1 Personal information is:
  a information in your portfolio
  b your employer's opinion of your work
  c information about yourself, such as qualities, skills, age, address
  d any information you write down

2 CV means:
  a as much information as possible about your past life
  b current value of your job
  c brief information about what you've done in your life
  d current vacancy advertisement

3 Which of these qualities would be useful for employment in caring?
  a patience
  b being trustworthy
  c reliability
  d all three

4 The best way to find out about local jobs is in:
  a national newspaper
  b local newspaper
  c *Yellow Pages*
  d school library

5 Other ways to find out about jobs would be from:
  a your next door neighbour
  b your parent's employers
  c Careers and Guidance Adviser
  d all three

6 Careers and Guidance Advisers are a good source of help as they will:
  a give practice interviews and advise you about your suitability for a job
  b tell your parents about availability of local jobs
  c write job advertisements
  d write your CV for you

7 When you have applied for a job, the next stage is:
  a going to the interview
  b being asked to attend an interview
  c being measured for the uniform
  d being appointed

8 When you attend an interview you are *most* likely to be asked:
  a why you want the job
  b to write an essay
  c what television programmes you like
  d whether you have any pets

Scoring

If you got:

- between 1 and 3 – you need to brush up on your knowledge and ask advice.

- between 4 and 6 – your understanding of this element is reasonable. Check that you understand the work you have covered.

- 7 and above – your understanding of how to plan finding a job for yourself is very good.

Useful addresses and organisations

The following organisations may be able to help you with information and advice. However, remember that they are busy, and don't overwhelm them with long lists of questions. Some may charge a small fee for carrying out research.

Action on Smoking and Health (ASH)
109 Gloucester Place
London
W1H 4EJ

Alcohol Concern
Waterbridge House
32-36 Loman Street
London
SE1 0EE

ASHA (Asian Women's Resource Centre)
27 Sautley Street
London
SW4 7QE

British Diabetic Association
10 Queen Anne Street
London
W1M 0BD

British Red Cross Society (BRCS)
9 Grosvenor Crescent
London
SW1X 7EJ

Brook Advisory Centres
Brook Central Office
165 Gray's Inn Road
London
WC1X 8UD

Child Poverty Action Group
4th Floor
1-5 Bath Street
London
EC1V 9PY

Children's Legal Centre
20 Compton Centre
London
N1 2UN

Citizens Advice Bureaux
Myddleton House
115-123 Pentonville Road
London
N1 9LZ

Commission For Racial Equality
Elliott House
10-12 Allington Street
London
SW1E 5EH

CRY-SIS Support Group
B.M. CRY-SIS
London
WC1N 3XX

Cystic Fybrosis Trust
Alexandra House
5 Blyth Road
Bromley
Kent
BR1 3RS

Down's Syndrome Association (DSA)
155 Mitcham Road
Tooting
London
SW17 9PG

Equal Opportunities Commission
Overseas House
Quay Street
Manchester
M3 3HN

Family Planning Association (FPA)
27-35 Mortimer Street
London
W1N 7RJ

Gingerbread
16-17 Clerkenwell Close
London
EC1R 0AA

Greenpeace
36 Earlham Street
London
N7

Health Education Authority
78 New Oxford Street
London
WC1H 1AH

MENCAP (Royal Society for Mentally Handicapped Children and Adults)
Mencap National Centre
123 Golden Lane
London
EC1Y 0RT

MIND (National Association for Mental Health)
Granta House
15-19 Broadway
Stratford
London
E15 4BQ

Narcotics Anonymous
PO Box 417
London
SW10 0DP

National Asthma Campaign
Providence House
Providence Place
London
N1 0NT

National Childbirth Trust
Alexandra House
Oldham Terrace
Acton
London
W3 6NH

NSPCC (National Society for the Prevention of Cruelty to Children)
National Centre
42 Curtain Road
London
EC2A 3NH

SENSE (National Deafblind and Rubella Association)
11-13 Clifton Terrace
Finsbury Park
London
N4 3SR

Shelter
88 Old Street
London
EC1V 9HU

Scope (Formerly The Spastics Society)
12 Park Crescent
London
W1N 4EQ

Terrence Higgins Trust
52-54 Gray's Inn Road
London
WC1X 8JU

Women's Aid Federation
PO Box 391
Bristol
BS99 7WS

Quiz answers

Element 1.1, page 43

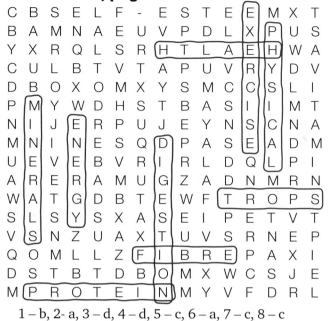

1 – b, 2- a, 3 – d, 4 – d, 5 – c, 6 – a, 7 – c, 8 – c

Element 1.2, page 62

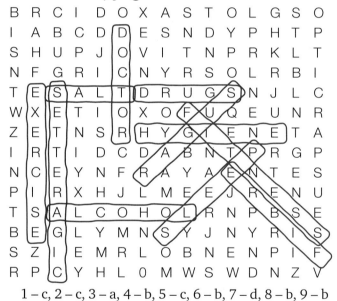

1 – c, 2 – c, 3 – a, 4 – b, 5 – c, 6 – b, 7 – d, 8 – b, 9 – b

Element 2.1, page 88

1 – b, 2 – a, 3 – c, 4 – b, 5 – c, 6 – c, 7 – d, 8 – c

Element 2.2, page 102

1 – d, 2 – c, 3 – b, 4 – b, 5 – d, 6 – a, 7 – c, 8 – b, 9 – d, 10 – b

Element 2.3, page 115

1 – b, 2 – c, 3 – b, 4 – a, 5 – b, 6 – c, 7 – c, 8 – b, 9 – d, 10 – b

Element 3.1, page 131

1 – a, 2 – c, 3 – b, 4 – b, 5 – a, 6 – a, 7 – a, 8 – c

Element 3.2, page 142

1 – b, 2 – c, 3 – c, 4 – a, 5 – d, 6 – c, 7 – b, 8 – d

Element 3.3, page 153

1 – c, 2 – c, 3 – d, 4 – b, 5 – d, 6 – a, 7 – b, 8 – a

Core skills coverage grid

Page	Activity/Assignment	Application of Number			Communication				Information Technology			
		1.1	1.2	1.3	1.1	1.2	1.3	1.4	1.1	1.2	1.3	1.4
15	Using percentages	*	*									
18	Bar charts	*	*	*								
19	Using pictograms	*	*	*								
21	Using measurements	*	*	*								
23	Conversion graphs	*	*	*								
25	Spreadsheets	*	*						*	*	*	
26	Foods	*		*		*	*	*	*	*	*	
28	**Mean, mode and range**	*	*	*								
32	What is health?					*						
34	Added vitamins and minerals							*				
34	Dietary guidelines							*				
35	What I eat					*						
37	How much exercise?	*	*	*		*						
38	Tracy											
39	Recreational activities	*	*	*		*						
40	Something to do											
40	Recreation and you	*	*	*		*						
41	**Improve health and well-being**	*	*	*	*	*	*		*	*	*	
45	Types of need					*						
46	Client needs											
46	Meeting needs					*						
47	Health risks				*	*						
51	Poor diet					*						
54	Contraception				*	*	*	*				
56	Social settings					*						
57	Life changes				*	*						
58	A number of changes					*						
59	The effects of change				*	*						
60	Support services							*				
61	**The Park View Centre**				*	*	*		*	*	*	
66	Seeking information							*				
69	Play				*			*				
79	Newspaper cuttings							*				
79	Differences				*	*		*				
82	Jamal's life					*		*				
83	Lifestyle changes				*	*		*				
85	Making choices				*	*		*				
86	**Life span chart**	*	*	*		*	*	*			*	
90	The holiday club					*		*				
92	Friend wanted					*						
92	Friendly discussion				*	*						
94	Discussion				*							
95	Parenting				*	*						
95	Changes						*					
97	Good things					*						
98	Family matters				*	*		*				
100	**Relationships chart**				*	*	*	*	*	*	*	
104	Alike and different					*						
105	Children's choice				*	*		*				
109	Breaking down barriers					*	*					
110	Being fed				*	*						
112	Help to be mobile						*					
113	Caring for older people					*		*				
114	**Clients and carers**				*	*		*				
118	My area				*	*	*	*				
119	Local services				*	*	*	*				
120	Local voluntary services				*	*	*	*				
120	See for yourself				*							
121	Care providers and jobs						*	*				
125	Match them up						*	*				
127	Which one?						*					
129	Which is it?						*					
129	Jobs and skills						*	*				
130	**Mr and Mrs Underwood**				*	*	*	*				
134	How do others see me?				*							
135	This is me					*						
136	My qualities				*							
136	Improved caring				*		*					
140	Two suitable jobs					*		*				
141	**Which job first?**				*	*		*				
148	Write your own CV				*	*			*	*	*	
148	Job application				*	*		*				
149	Application analysis					*		*				
149	Letter of application					*						
150	Using application forms				*							
152	Job advertisements				*							
152	**The careers exhibition**				*	*	*		*	*	*	

Index

Turn to the page number shown in **bold** in this index if you want a quick explanation of what a word or phrase means.

Academic skills	**134**, 135, 136
Addiction	48
Adolescence	74-6, 96
Adulthood	76-7, 96
Alcoholism	**47**-8
Ante-natal	**122**
Applicant	**145**
Application form	30, **145**, 150
Assertive quality	**93**
Atherosclerosis	50
Averages, number	27-8
Babies	66-8
Bacteria	**53**
Barriers	**107**, 108
Body language	6, 9, **151**
Bonds	**68**, 92
Brainstorm	**47**
Bronchitis	**48**
Career progression	**132**
Careers and Guidance Advisers	137-8, 144
Carer	**46**, 103, 109
Caring	6, 117, 137, 138-9
Child care	126-7, 139
Childhood	69-73, 96
Circumstances	**134**
Citizens Advice Bureau	60, **146**, 154
Client	**46**, 103, 105, 109-12
Client groups	**46**
Communication	6-12, 68, 111
Community services	120
Computers	2, 24-6
Confidentiality	106, 108
Constipation	**33**, 51
Contraception	**54**
Core skills	**134**, 135
Couch potato	**36**
CV (curriculum vitae)	**145**, 147-8, 150
Decimal fractions	13-14
Deficiency disease	**51**
Dementia	**78**
Diagnose	**122**

Diagnostic	**124**
Diet	32-6, 50-1
Dietitian	**124**
Digest	**33**
Drugs	**49**-50
Economics	**83**
Emotional development	65-6, 68, 69-73, 75, 77, 79
Emotional needs	44-6, **58**, 60, 109, 112
Emphysema	**48**
Employment, initial	**133**
Employment contract	**146**
Environment	**67**, 81
Exercise	36-40, 55-6
Financial commitments	**84**
Foster parent	**121**
Fractions	13
Genes	**66**
Goals, long/short term	**41**
Graphs	24-6
Health	32, 44-56
Health care	117, 119, 139
Health and Safety at Work Act (1974)	5
Hygiene	51-3, 111
Hypothermia	**78**
Identity	**90**, 104
Income	**84**
Indirect care	**120**, 128-9
Infancy	66-8
Infertility	**55**
Inhibitions	**47**
Initiative	**144**
Inpatient	**117**
Intellectual development	**39**, 67-8, 69-73, 74, 77, 79
Intellectual needs	44-6, 109
Interaction	**68**
Interview	2, **144**, 151
Interviewee	**152**
Job roles	122-4, 126-7, 128-9
Jobs	133-4, 137-8, 144, 145-6
Letters, formal	3, 10, **145**, 148, 150
Life stages	44, 46, 57-60, 66, 76, 77, 86, 89, 96-100
Lifestyle	**32**
Listening skills	6

Mean and mode	27-8
Measurement	19-23
Memoranda (memos)	11
Menopause	76
Mobility	**32**, 37, 112
Mother figure	**68**
Mutually supportive relationships	**93**
National Health Service (NHS)	117, 121
National Record of Achievement	**148**
NHS and Community Care Act (1990)	117
Number application	
averages	27-8
decimals	13-14
fractions	13
graphs	16-19, 24-6
measurement	19-23
percentages	13, 15
Nursing	114, 122, 139
Occupational therapy	123, 139
Old age	78-9, 96
Osteoporosis	**130**
Outpatient	**117**
Parents	77, 94-5
Percentages	13, 15
Personality	135
Physical development	65-6, 67, 69-73, 74, 76, 78
Physical needs	44-6, 109
Physiotherapy	123, 139
Plaque	**53**
Positive relationships	**96**-7
Post-menopause	**48**
Post-natal	**122**
Potential	**74**
Pregnancy	54
Presentations	2, 3, 7-8
Priorities	**84**
Private sector	117, 119, 121
Professional	**119**
Prospective	**143**
Puberty	74
Pulses	**33**
Qualifications	138-9
Qualities	92, 135, 136, 137
Recreational activity	**39-40**
Recruitment	**145-6**

References	**132**, 146
Relationships	**91**, **93**, **96-7**, 98
client/carer	103-8
family	80, 94-5
life stages	76, 77, 89, 96-100
things going wrong	97-8, 107-8
at work	93
Relaxation	60
Remedial care	**124**
Reports	12
Respite care	**120**
Sector	**117**
Self-concept	**90**, 134-5, 136
Self-esteem	**32**, 73, **90**, 96, 98, 112
Self-image	**73**, 80, **90**
Sexual intercourse	**54**-5, **94**
Skills	**134**, 135, 136
Smoking	48-9, 154
Social development	56, 65-6, 68-73, 75, 77, 79, 90
Social needs	44-6, 109
Social Services	117, 118, 121
Social work	126, 139
Statutory service	**118**
Stress	59-60
Stroke	**50**
Study skills	2-3
Support	**60**
Talking skills	6, 7, 8
Telephone skills	3, 7
Temperament	**134**, 135
Therapeutic	**124**
Ultrasound scan	**124**
Values	**72**
Vitamins	33, 34, 51
Vocational	**134**, 135
Voluntary sector	60, 117, 119-20, 121, 154
Well-being	**32**, 98
Writing skills	10

Acknowledgements

Acquisitions: Sonia Clark
Administration: Jenny Goode
Editorial: Gaynor Roberts/Sue Mildenhall
Marketing: Jane Lewis
Production: Hamish Adamson
Staff design: Maria Pritchard
Design: Ken Vail Graphic Design

Illustrations and other printed matter

The authors and publishers are grateful to the following for permission to reproduce copyright material. If any acknowledgement has been omitted, this will be rectified at the earliest opportunity.

Page 35: *The Balance of Good Health*, reproduced by permission of the Health Education Authority.

Page 36: Height and weight chart by permission of the Health Education Authority.

Page 44: Table *Meeting basic health needs* reproduced by permission of Stanley Thornes Publishers.

Page 47: Leaflet *So you think you can handle it*, Department of Health and leaflet *No excuses*, Department of Health and BBC.

Page 55: Leaflet *Fingers crossed*, published by Southampton Health Promotion Services.

Photographs
Len Cross: pp.4, 5, 6, 7, 8, 12, 31, 39, 40, 45, 56, 58, 69, 78, 79, 82, 83, 91, 93, 97, 98, 103, 106, 114, 118, 130, 140, 143, 148, 149, 150
Images: pp.39, 54, 85
The Image Bank: p.77
BSIP/Science Photo Library: p.50
Cover photograph: GNVQ students at John Ruskin College, photographed by Len Cross.

Cartoons and line artwork: John Green